THE NUCLEAR POWER DEBATE

THE NUCLEAR POWER DEBATE
A Guide to the Literature

Jerry W. Mansfield

GARLAND PUBLISHING, INC. • NEW YORK & LONDON
1984

Library of Congress Cataloging in Publication Data

Mansfield, Jerry W.
The nuclear power debate.

Includes index.
1. Atomic power—Bibliography. I. Title.
Z5160.M36 1984   016.62148   83-48255
[TK9145]
ISBN 0-8240-9102-7 (alk. paper)

Cover design by Larry Walczak

Printed on acid-free, 250-year-life paper
Manufactured in the United States of America

To My Parents
William and Beverley

CONTENTS

Preface

All over this world there are people who watch complacently as citizens in other parts of the United States and abroad rise up against nuclear power or as others speak in its favor. Often the two views are contradictory and the general public is confused about the real issues. One day there is talk of a nuclear power plant to be built near your home or workplace and suddenly, you have neighbors and friends who have never publicly supported anything or who have never before protested against an issue poised for action. People on both sides of the nuclear power debate will begin to seek information to support their views and to further educate themselves on the crucial issues.

This annotated bibliography will prove to be a starting point to that education and awareness of the issues. The nuclear power debate is a complicated one and it is hoped that through the reading of the books in this list, most of which should be available in medium to large public libraries, citizens will be far more aware and able to take a firm stand in their belief, for whatever side of the question they support.

Since the 1979 Three Mile Island incident the marketplace has been flooded with books on nuclear power and alternative energy sources. Many of these were written overnight to satisfy the public demand for more information on radiation, wastes, nuclear hazards, transportation and other related

topics. The thirst for nuclear energy information was insatiable and books were followed by
magazine articles and newspaper stories. Some
books were written by knowledgeable experts while
others were haphazardly put together merely to
capitalize on this nuclear information craze.

Thousands of government and industrial technical reports are available on nuclear energy.
Even more journal articles have been written in the
popular and scientific literature. It would be a
massive undertaking to identify and read all that
has been written since 1975 on the nuclear power
question. This bibliography is, therefore, limited
to books of a non-technical, general interest
nature written primarily in the last decade. No
attempt was made to exclude titles or works by
certain authors. Rather, the intention is to
present a cross-section of reading materials in a
balanced format.

In the last few years more books have been
written *against* nuclear power than *for* this energy
source. One may speculate that those people who
are against any movement are more vocal than the
supporters, that it is easier to publish and market
an anti-nuclear book, or that nuclear activists
must try twice as hard to get their point across.
There are also well-financed and highly visible
lobbying groups against nuclear power, but smaller,
quieter ones for nuclear growth. As one of the
authors in this bibliography suggests, nuclear
advocates seem less vocal because they are lost in
the din of the ignorant and, in time, even nuclear
activists will cross over to the other side out of
necessity.

The intent of this research guide is not to
say that one side is right and another is wrong.
Rather, it is to provide a selected sampling of
quality, non-technical books from all viewpoints
in the nuclear power debate.

The book is arranged in three sections.
First there are the books which have been deter-
mined to be PRO-NUCLEAR, followed by those which
are decidedly ANTI-NUCLEAR. The last section
consists of some books which are NEUTRAL treatments

of the debate. In all sections the books are arranged alphabetically by the authors' last names unless the book is a collection of essays or has no author, in which case it is listed by the title.

JWM

Pro-Nuclear

1.   Beckman, Petr. THE HEALTH HAZARDS OF <u>NOT</u>
        GOING NUCLEAR. Boulder, CO: Golem, 1976.

Starting off this section is a powerful pro-nuclear book with a unique angle. In less than polite tones Beckman critizes Ralph Nader's ignorance of nuclear safety and states that the nuclear debate, if there is anything to debate, is replete with myths, distortions, and falsehoods. We are informed that an atomic explosion in a nuclear plant is physically impossible due to the type of uranium used as a power plant fuel. Several times the author makes it clear to the reader that "the point of this book is not to argue how dangerous fossils are, but that nuclear power is safer." The book is full of anger toward all the unqualified people who speak out against nuclear power. Examples include Nobel Prize winners who are distinguished in fields unconnected with nuclear power but who speak against it as if the Nobel Laureate title makes them instant experts in all areas of science. Further verbal lashings are given to the media who have a bias toward anti-nuclear causes, the misleading

statistics which are used, and of course,
the environmental and political action
groups which spring up like mushrooms at the
mere mention of the word "nuclear."

2.   Bromberg, Joan Lisa. FUSION: SCIENCE,
        POLITICS, AND THE INVENTION OF A NEW
        ENERGY SOURCE. Cambridge, MA: MIT Press,
        1982.

        From a historical viewpoint Dr. Bromberg
provides a very readable, quasi-scientific
account of controlled thermonuclear research
(CTR). For over thirty years researchers
have been trying to demonstrate that nuclear
fusion reactions between light elements can
provide a new energy source. Concentrating
on the political and organizational aspects
of the Magnetic Fusion Program in the U.S.,
we learn of the early security clamps placed
on the research centers of Los Alamos, Oak
Ridge, and Princeton. The classified aspect
of CTR was weakened in 1958 in time for the
Second Geneva Conference where all countries
with fusion programs displayed their pro-
gress. The American exhibit, a flashy
mechanical display, was the Sherwood Specta-
cular which attracted many visitors. Project Sherwood was the name given to the Los
Alamos project. The latter portions of
Fusion are devoted to the effects which the
many changes in leadership, industrial and
political, have had on the various research
programs. Albeit this is not a book direct-
ly concerned with the nuclear controversy
of the 1980s, Bromberg's account may be the
first official history of any nation's
fusion research and for that it is a noteworthy document. The book was commissioned
by the Office of Magnetic Fusion Energy of
the U.S. Department of Energy.

3. Bupp, Irvin C., and Jean-Claude Derian.
    LIGHT WATER: HOW THE NUCLEAR DREAM
    DISSOLVED. New York: Basic, 1978.

    After World War II the hopes for nuclear
    energy as a power source were almost real-
    ized and became a greater possibility after
    the 1973 OPEC oil embargo. This book is an
    interpretation of how the most promising
    reactor technology, light water, seemed to be
    the answer to the nuclear energy need. The
    downfall came in the manner in which the U.S.
    managed and presented the need for nuclear
    power to the citizens. Distrust was the
    result and these emotions are still the
    driving force behind the nuclear safety
    controversy. The involvement of the corpor-
    ations, politicians, and the citizens groups
    for and against nuclear energy are clearly
    charted in this historical assessment of
    what is, according to the authors, a "dream
    dissolved."

4. Cameron, I.R. NUCLEAR FISSION REACTORS.
    New York: Plenum, 1982.

    This is a sound and thorough introduc-
    tory text on fission technology. A diverse
    presentation of scientific and technical
    ideas is provided in a light, readable and
    clear manner. Cameron discusses the physics
    of atoms as it relates to nuclear reaction
    theory and follows with explanations of
    nuclear fuel, radiation damage, and basic
    heat transfer. Four chapters are devoted
    to the main reactor types including light-
    water, fast-breeder reactors, heavy-water,
    and gas-cooled systems. The author rounds
    out the book with a very long chapter on
    the safety and environmental effects of
    nuclear power including a brief account of
    Three Mile Island.

5.   Cantelon, Philip L., and Robert C. Williams.
        CRISIS CONTAINED: THE DEPARTMENT OF
        ENERGY AT THREE MILE ISLAND. Carbondale,
        IL: Southern Illinois University Press,
        1982.

        The Department of Energy commissioned
        the authors to chronicle the months of acti-
        vity following the 1979 incident at Three
        Mile Island. DOE's involvement included
        monitoring, analyzing, and coordinating the
        radiation data from TMI. The conclusion
        reached was that human errors were to blame,
        not technological failures. Two useful
        appendices include a roster of all personnel
        investigating the TMI aftermath and a
        synoptic chronology of events.

6.   Clark, Ronald W. THE GREATEST POWER ON
        EARTH: THE INTERNATIONAL RACE FOR SUPRE-
        MACY. New York: Harper, 1981.
        (Published in England as *The Greatest
        Power on Earth: The Story of Nuclear
        Fission*. London: Sidgwick & Jackson,
        1980.)

        The major portion of this work covers
        the history of the discovery of atomic
        fission in 1938 through the wartime efforts
        to produce nuclear weapons in Britain, the
        U.S., Germany, and Russia. Careful reading
        of the book will make clear the distinction
        between fission and fusion energy. Clark
        provides a brief account of the development
        of the hydrogen bomb, the attempts to uti-
        lize fission power as an energy source, and
        he touches upon the growing public awareness
        of the radiation perils associated with
        peaceful and military uses of nuclear power.
        In his concluding paragraph he says, "It
        would be tragic if a limited nuclear
        exchange, halted after each side had exper-
        ienced the agony of one city put to the bomb,
        were necessary to bring men to their senses
        and to realize , at last, that there are no
        victors in nuclear war."

7. Cochran, Thomas B. THE LIQUID METAL FAST
   BREEDER REACTOR. Baltimore: Johns
   Hopkins University, 1974.

   The Liquid Metal Fast Breeder Reactor
   (LMFBR) has been subject to considerable
   scrutiny and criticism in the U.S. despite
   its success and expansion in the UK, France,
   Germany, Italy, Japan, and the Soviet Union.
   Mr. Cochran takes a serious look at the
   costs and the environmental arguments which
   favor the LMFBR use in the U.S. Relying
   heavily upon AEC reports he assesses fuel
   cycle costs, performance, and even uranium
   supply and demand. The author tends to be
   pessimistic about the future of LMFBRs and
   instead advocates thermal reactors and a
   continued search for responsible energy
   alternatives. A critical analysis is made
   between the LMFBR and high-water reactors
   and Cochran suggests that perhaps the U.S.
   should wait to see what new information and
   technology is available by 1986 to ensure
   that the decision made is one which will
   last into the next century. The problems of
   waste storage, safe fuel transportation,
   and reactor safety are all touched upon in
   this critical look at the liquid metal fast
   breeder reactor.

8. Cohen, Bernard L. NUCLEAR SCIENCE AND
   SOCIETY. Garden City, NY: Anchor, 1974.

   A well-read individual of nuclear topics
   would understand and appreciate the correla-
   tions made by Dr. Cohen between nuclear
   research and society's needs. In this work
   we are provided with some benefits of
   radiation not generally known, such as its
   ability to retard food spoilage, control

insects, and aid in genetic crop research.
Other uses include the desalting of sea-
water as well as peacetime ship and rocket
propulsion. Along with a historical view of
society's use, value, and perceptions of
energy, the author provides concise and
graphic descriptions of how fission reactors
and fast breeder reactors work. Finally,
brief coverage is given for the peaceful
uses of nuclear explosives, nuclear warfare,
and nuclear weaponry.

9.   Cottrell, Alan, Sir. HOW SAFE IS NUCLEAR
        ENERGY? Exeter, NH: Heinemann, 1981.

        This is a very factual book about how
reactors produce energy, how wastes are
released, the effects of varying levels of
radiation, and the question of safety. The
author is admittedly pro-nuclear but here he
presents all of the facts and allows the
reader to decide for himself. If nuclear
power is unsafe, then we should reject it.
If it is safe or can be made safer, then
let's get rid of the fear and get on with it.
Should this world go forth with increased
production and dependence on nuclear power,
then we owe future generations a safe and
reliable energy system. Sir Alan's comments
are sure to provoke both the anti-nukes with
his strong support for nuclear power and the
nuclear establishment with his concerns about
the fracture of pressure vessels.

10. Garvey, Gerald. NUCLEAR POWER AND SOCIAL
PLANNING. Lexington, MA: Lexington,
1977.

Believing that America's commitment to
nuclear power is irreversible, this Princeton
professor of politics advocates that we learn
how best to control nuclear development. The
technical, economic, and socio-political
factors affecting the question of control are
carefully examined. Garvey discusses the
need to switch from fission to fusion energy
and asks if power parks, or nuplexes
(nuclear powered agro-chemico-industrial
complexes) as they are sometimes called, are
a solution. Many useful charts and diagrams
help the reader to understand the issues and,
perhaps for the undecided, aid in making up
their own mind in this debate.

11. Glasstone, Samuel, and Walter H. Jordan.
NUCLEAR POWER AND ITS ENVIRONMENTAL
EFFECTS. New York: American Nuclear
Society, 1980.

Contrary to what anti-nuclear critics
say, Drs. Glasstone and Jordan state that it
is possible for nuclear power to account for
one-fifth of the U.S. electricity generated
by 1990. They do realize, however, that a
successful nuclear program in the U.S. will
depend on the public's perception of its
environmental and safety aspects. Knowing
this, the authors clearly describe the
environmental effects of nuclear power and
explain the safety measures taken to ensure
the safe operation of power plants. The
needless confusion which exists on this
topic is cleared by their numerous illus-
trations, examples, and their combined years
of first-hand experience.

12.   Grenon, M. THE NUCLEAR APPLE AND THE SOLAR
          ORANGE: ALTERNATIVES IN WORLD ENERGY.
          Elmsford, NY: Pergamon, 1981.

          Affiliated with the International Insti-
      tute for Applied Systems Analysis in
      Austria, the author utilizes his "watchdog"
      position to assess the world energy situa-
      tion. His non-technical discussion includes
      heavy emphasis on nuclear and solar energy
      as the primary sources of world energy.
      This overview of the energy dilemma also
      includes the merits of geothermal energy and
      coal. Not limited to U.S. energy problems,
      this work covers the global question and the
      need for alternative energy sources.

13.   The Harvard Nuclear Study Group. LIVING
          WITH NUCLEAR WEAPONS. Cambridge, MA:
          Harvard University Press, 1983.

          The President of Harvard University,
      Derek Bok, urged the University to take a
      stand on the issue of nuclear weapons and
      Living With Nuclear Weapons is their state-
      ment. The work is a valuable history of how
      the present nuclear predicament developed
      and serves as a guide to policy options for
      coping with the situation. One of the book's
      major points is that the public spends far
      too much time worrying about all of the
      fringe areas of nuclear power such as
      mechanical/human errors and sabotage rather
      than the real dangers of war in Third World
      countries who are newcomers to the nuclear
      weapon arena. Numerous arguments are made
      for ICBMs, MX missiles, and more non-contro-
      versial weaponry. Although this work does
      not inform readers how to get rid of the
      nuclear war threat, it will nevertheless be
      a landmark, controversial book on the
      nuclear power debate.

14.   Hertsgaard, Mark. NUCLEAR INC.: THE MEN AND
          MONEY BEHIND NUCLEAR ENERGY. New York:
          Pantheon, 1983.

          This work is a history of the atomic-
       industrial complex and the people and corpor-
       ations which make it function. The author
       interviewed executives from the major firms
       which hope to sell reactors, construct the
       power plants, and provide the nuclear power
       generated electricity to make for a nuclear
       powered America. Briefly mentioned is the
       relationship which these dozen or so firms
       have with big business and government. A
       few of the executives reveal the "Atomic
       Brotherhood's" (that's what they call them-
       selves) plans and strategies for making
       America dependent on safe and efficient
       nuclear power.

15.   Hoyle, Fred, Sir, and Geoffrey Hoyle.
          COMMONSENSE IN NUCLEAR ENERGY. New York:
          Freeman, 1980.

          Many myths surround the nuclear power
       industry and this father and son team try to
       dispel some of them. Arguing that fossil
       fuels will run out someday, they develop
       the case for nuclear power as a clean,
       viable, and safe alternative. The authors,
       both renowned scientists and conservation-
       ists, point out that technologists and
       environmentalists can and must learn to live
       harmoniously. This is a well-written and
       easy-to-read pro-nuclear book.

16.   Hoyle, Fred, *Sir*. ENERGY OR EXTINCTION?
            THE CASE FOR NUCLEAR ENERGY. London:
            Heinemann, 1979.

            Forever the crusader for nuclear energy,
        Hoyle illustrates that we will someday run
        out of oil and that we really have no prac-
        tical alternative fuel. Although the public
        is favorable to solar energy and the media
        remains optimistic, the technology to har-
        ness this and other alternative energy
        sources on a large scale just does not exist.
        It is safe, reliable, and power can be cre-
        ated without fast-breeder reactors like the
        CANDU (Canadian-Deuterium-Uranium) type
        reactor. In his usual controversial fashion
        the author points out that some of the anti-
        nuclear campaigns are politically inspired
        as a means to weaken the West. Written in
        non-scientific terms, this book serves as an
        important introduction to the nuclear energy
        controversy.

17.   Imai, Ryukichi, and Henry S. Rowen.
            NUCLEAR ENERGY AND NUCLEAR PROLIFERATION:
            JAPANESE AND AMERICAN VIEWS. Boulder,
            CO: Westview, 1980.

            This elementary foreign policy book
        treats the sensitive international issue of
        nuclear nonproliferation. When President
        Carter came into office in 1977 he promised
        better U.S.-Japanese relations and a closely
        guarded nonproliferation policy. Carter
        announced that the U.S. was going to defer
        the use of plutonium in existing reactors
        and that a restructuring of breeder reactor
        research and development was to occur which
        would stress safety rather than early
        commercialization. This was in direct con-
        flict with an existing agreement with Japan
        which pledged to forge ahead. The authors
        of this work were involved in behind-the-
        scenes activity to arrange for a solution
        amenable to both countries. Mr. Imai, as

general manager of engineering of the Japan
Atomic Power Company and as Japanese mini-
sterial advisor, and Mr. Rowen, a Stanford
Professor, former Rand Corporation president,
former assistant director of the U.S. Bureau
of the Budget, and deputy assistant secretary
of defense, spent years working out the
details and acting as go-betweens on this
vital issue. This is their side of the
story.

18.   Knief, Ronald Allen. NUCLEAR ENERGY TECH-
         NOLOGY: THEORY AND PRACTICE OF COMMERCIAL
         NUCLEAR POWER. Washington, DC:
         Hemisphere, 1981.

       Knief's book is intended to be an author-
atative reference book on nuclear energy
technology for the scientist as well as the
student. Theory and the practical aspects
of nuclear technology are provided to assist
in the understanding of current practices,
reactors, and future prospects. A review
of fuel cycles, reactor design, and reactor
safety fundamentals is provided. The status
of nuclear energy worldwide is presented by
this former manager of training at Three
Mile Island. Extensive bibliographies
follow each chapter.

19.   Lapp, Ralph Eugene. NADER'S NUCLEAR ISSUES.
         Greenwich, CT: Fact Systems, 1975.

       Dr. Lapp declares war on Ralph Nader's
charge that "nuclear fission power is
unsafe, unnecessary, and unreliable" in this
battle of words. The format for the majority of the book is that of actual Nader
comments followed by a rebuttal from the
author. Numerous appendices are included
which contain endorsements for nuclear power
from scientists, congressmen, and Nobel
Prize winners.

20.   Libby, Leona Marshall. THE URANIUM PEOPLE.
          New York: Crane, Russak/Scribners, 1979.

          This is a historical book of the atomic
       stars who were involved in the early years
       of discovery and development of atomic
       energy. Dr. Libby was the youngest and the
       only female member of the group which built
       the first reactor. As a physicist she
       worked in the company of Robert Oppenheimer,
       Glenn Seaborg, and other Nobel Laureates-to-
       be. A special insight into the problems of
       physics and chemistry which the scientists
       encountered is provided. However, more than
       telling what was scientifically interesting
       about the uranium-plutonium project, Libby
       has a flair for telling what was human and
       fascinating about the people involved. She
       often reveals the human thoughts of the
       scientists as they worked out scientific and
       moral problems. This documentary with black
       and white photos ends with the establishment
       of the Atomic Energy Commission, the Russian
       A-bomb, and the H-bomb controversy.

21.   Lilienthal, David E. ATOMIC ENERGY: A NEW
          START. New York: Harper, 1980.

          This is the premier history of nuclear
       energy research and development in the U.S.
       written by a man who once headed the
       Tennessee Valley Authority and who was the
       first chairman of the Atomic Energy Commi-
       ssion. As an advocate of nuclear responsi-
       bility, Lilienthal argues for safer, peaceful
       uses of nuclear power and the elimination of
       nuclear weapons. Some predictions of the
       future of nuclear energy are also ventured.

22. Longstaff, Malcolm. UNLOCKING THE ATOM: A
    HUNDRED YEARS OF NUCLEAR ENERGY.
    London: Muller, 1980.

Most of the recent books on the development of nuclear energy dwell on the political
and moral arguments yet few can succeed in
covering the technological aspects in a
manner which is appealing to the general
reader like *Unlocking the Atom*. The book
begins with the story of the discovery of
uranium, radioactivity, and fission and
discusses the work leading to the bombs of
Nagasaki and Hiroshima. Full chapters each
are devoted to safety, energy, the place of
nuclear power today, and other uses of
nuclear power. Well-chosen photographs
complement the text. This easy-to-read
history was written by a twenty-four year
veteran of the United Kingdom Atomic Energy
Authority.

23. McCracken, Samuel. THE WAR AGAINST THE ATOM.
    New York: Basic, 1982.

This is another non-technical, historical
review of the atomic industry. McCracken
examines individuals and organizations
behind the anti-nuclear movement in order to
more fully understand the roots of resistance.
In his conclusion the author attacks the
views of five well-known anti-nuclear
activists. This critical last chapter alone
makes the reading of the book worthwhile.
This is very much a one-sided, pro-nuclear
essay describing the battle against the
nuclear industry.

24.   Maddox, John.   BEYOND THE ENERGY CRISIS.
            New York: McGraw-Hill, 1975.

            In response to the OPEC oil crisis, this
        British physicist pleads for reduced oil
        consumption and the development of alterna-
        tive sources of fuel. The favored source
        for the author is nuclear generated power.
        This is a factual account of the economic,
        political, and technical difficulties of
        converting nuclear power into a viable source
        of energy. This would be a more valuable
        book if it had tables and graphs illustrating
        the author's points, but nevertheless, it is
        a good synopsis of the energy crisis and has
        some positive solutions.

25.   Mann, Martin.   PEACETIME USES OF ATOMIC
            ENERGY. Rev ed.   New York: Viking,
            1961.

            Here is an excellent book extolling the
        usefulness of atomic energy in everyday life.
        Mann illustrates how our quality of life
        has been enhanced by atomic energy, how it
        has actually protected out health, and how
        it aids us in answering the how and the why
        of the universe. Numerous illustrations
        help the reader to understand the positive
        impact of atomic power. This should be
        read in conjunction with the Cohen book,
        Nuclear Science and Society. (Item number 8)

26.   THE NUCLEAR POWER CONTROVERSY. Englewood
          Cliffs, NJ: Prentice-Hall, 1976.

          The American Assembly, an affiliate of
Columbia University, has sponsored this
series of papers on the nuclear debate.
This book contains five general essays by
pro-nuclear specialists and one by a nuclear
critic as a balance. Topics covered include
reactor safety, including waste storage, the
economics of nuclear power, a brief history
of the ups and downs in the twenty years of
nuclear power generation, the nuclear
regulatory process, the international aspects
of the controversy as well as nuclear proliferation, and the anti-nuclear power essay
which asks, "How much is too much?" This
collection of papers is intended to start a
dialogue on the subject of nuclear power
and to encourage the general public to
continue questioning the technologies and
policies of others which pervade their own
lives.

27.   Schmidt, Fred H., and David Bodansky. THE
          FIGHT OVER NUCLEAR POWER: THE ENERGY
          CONTROVERSY. San Francisco: Albion,
          1976. Foreword by Hans Bethe.

          Realizing that the U.S. needs energy,
that fossil fuels are limited, that uranium,
thorium, and breeder reactors can satisfy
the energy needs of the world for 100,000
years, and that nuclear power is safe, the
authors push for the urgent, responsible
development of nuclear power. The energy
alternatives heralded by other writers are
viewed as insufficient for large-scale
energy production. However, researchers
must continue to search for scientific break-
throughs in the area of alternative solutions to the dwindling fossil fuel supply.
The problems of nuclear power are not over-
looked and some solutions are offered which
are thought provoking.

28.   Seaborg, Glenn T., and William R. Corliss.
           MAN AND ATOM: BUILDING A NEW WORLD
           THROUGH TECHNOLOGY. New York: Dutton,
           1971.

           The apprehensions and concerns of anti-
       nuclear individuals are understood and an
       attempt is made to allay their fears by
       showing the peaceful applications of the
       atom. Nuclear power technology and research
       has given the world numerous medical,
       household, and outer space uses. Even
       greater than these are the future prospects
       for benefit to mankind in the areas of agri-
       cultural nuplexes and underwater exploration
       and habitation. With no intention of side-
       stepping the issue of nuclear energy in
       general, the authors contend that the
       scientific community will work out solutions
       to these problems and that right now our
       need is for a viable solution to the fossil
       fuel energy drain. Directed to the intelli-
       gent non-technical reader, this book has
       many useful photos and charts to reinforce
       its arguments.

29.   Smart, Ian. WORLD NUCLEAR ENERGY: TOWARD A
           BARGAIN OF CONFIDENCE. Baltimore:
           Johns Hopkins University Press, 1982.

           In 1977 and with a membership of just
       twenty people the International Consultative
       Group on Nuclear Energy (ICGNE) was formed
       to examine the uncertainties of the nuclear
       industry. *World Nuclear Energy* brings
       together eight of ICGNE's position papers
       written between 1978 and 1980 which cover
       international nuclear relationships, the
       history of world atomic cooperation, the
       economic and technical constraints of
       reactors, and nuclear plant construction.
       ICGNE supports an expanded program of inter-
       national cooperation in fast reactor develop-
       ment. The authors of these papers also

argue for an international program of
waste management and a demonstration of the
commercial feasibility of spent fuel repro-
cessing. Although they advocate a total
international cooperation and idea sharing
in nuclear power, they also realize that the
major roadblock to this is the fear of
weapons proliferation. The essays in this
book provide some valuable nuclear concerns,
some of which we will still be discussing
twenty years from now.

30.   Williams, Roger. THE NUCLEAR POWER DECI-
         SIONS: BRITISH POLICIES, 1953-78.
       London: Croom Helm, 1980.

         Twenty-five years of nuclear history is
traced in Great Britain and compared to
worldwide advancements in the nuclear industry. Non-technical discussions are provided
of the Magnox and AGR British reactors, the
light-water ones, PWR and BWR of the U.S.,
and the CANDU heavy-water reactor of Canada.
A brief background is given on how and why
these types of reactors were chosen by the
respective countries. The majority of the
book deals with the history of the
Advanced Gas-Cooled Reactor (AGR) and why it
was "best" for Great Britain. The latter
portion of this work covers the controversial
Windscale Decision dealing with the expansion
of a nuclear processing plant. Although
this has a purely British angle to it, *The
Nuclear Power Decisions* can serve as a
valuable historical guide to global decision
making on nuclear concerns.

31.   York, Herbert F.   THE ADVISORS: OPPENHEIMER,
          TELLER, AND THE SUPERBOMB.   New York:
          Freeman, 1976.

          With his insight and wisdom as father of
       the nuclear bomb, J. Robert Oppenheimer
       recommended in 1949 that the Atomic Energy
       Commission not develop a hydrogen bomb.   His
       arguments were social, political, and techno-
       logical, but he lost to a bright physicist,
       Edward Teller.   The result was the develop-
       ment of the hydrogen bomb by 1952 followed
       three years later by the same success in the
       Soviet Union.   This is a superb memoir of
       two men who were paramount in determining
       the nuclear course of America.   Any guide
       to the nuclear debate should include a
       history of the Teller-Oppenheimer connection
       even though this one is somewhat technical.

Anti-Nuclear

32.   Aldridge, Robert C.   FIRST STRIKE!: THE
      PENTAGON'S STRATEGY FOR NUCLEAR WAR.
      Boston: South End Press, 1983.

In the last few years the number of
scientists who once earned their living in
the nuclear industry but who have now turned
against nuclear power has increased drama-
tically. Aldridge is one of these individuals and up until 1973 was an engineer for
Lockheed Missiles & Space Co. *First Strike!*
is an insider's critique of the military-
industrial complex which adheres to the
philosophy that the U.S. is leaning toward
a first strike capability. The book goes
into great detail about ballistic missiles,
MX and cruise missiles, and other forms of
nuclear-based military technology. Written
for the general interest reader, Aldridge's
perspective lends much to the understanding
of why so many nuclear industry workers have
turned sour on nuclear power.

33.   ATOM'S EVE: ENDING THE NUCLEAR AGE, AN
           ANTHOLOGY. Edited by Mark Reader,
           Ronald Hardert, and Gerald L. Mouton.
           New York: McGraw-Hill, 1980.

       More than forty, fiery contributed essays
       make for lively reading in this anti-nuclear
       book. Some of the comments are very brief
       and others quite lengthy, but all have one
       premise--Earth will be uninhabitable or
       destroyed if something is not done now
       about nuclear power and its waste. Every-
       thing from Three Mile Island to health
       problems to nuclear war to cover-up cases is
       discussed. Some of the more notable contri-
       butors include Helen Caldicott, Barry
       Commoner, Jacques Cousteau, Vernon Jordan,
       Amory B. Lovins, and Lewis Mumford. An
       extensive checklist of energy alternatives
       and organizations, a calendar of major
       nuclear events since 1945, and a bibliography
       of nuclear books and films are appended.

34.   Beres, Louis Rene. TERRORISM AND GLOBAL
           SECURITY; THE NUCLEAR THREAT. Boulder,
           CO: Westview, 1979. (Westview Special
           Studies in National and International
           Terrorism)

       This is a political scientist's view
       of modern terrorism which points out that
       uncontrolled terrorism could pose a nuclear
       threat. Beres talks about preventive
       security measures, how to deal effectively
       with terrorist behavior, and he provides
       readers with his own preventive plan of
       international cooperation. The book is
       entirely devoted to the threat of terrorism
       and does not include discussions of the
       technical aspects of nuclear power. On the
       socio-political level this is an eloquently
       written and thought-provoking work directed
       toward the well-read nuclear individual.

35.   British Medical Association. Board of
       Science and Education. THE MEDICAL
       EFFECTS OF NUCLEAR WAR: THE REPORT OF
       THE BRITISH MEDICAL ASSOCIATION'S BOARD
       OF SCIENCE AND EDUCATION. New York:
       Wiley, 1983.

       Ever since the effects of nuclear war
   have been studied, many people have argued
   that all that there is to know about the
   topic is already known. However, as this
   book points out, the 1960s and 1970s saw
   nuclear testing malfunctions and the ozone
   layer controversy, both undetected after-
   effects. Only a year ago the situation of
   reduced sunlight due to the amount of soot
   in the atmosphere was discussed and may
   turn out to be the most detrimental of all
   nuclear war effects. The Board questions
   the governmental estimates of blast
   casualties and offers its own predictions.
   The example used is that of a Soviet attack
   on the UK of about 200 megatons, or over
   three tons of explosives for every inhab-
   itant of the British Isles. The level of
   the attack could be higher if cruise
   missiles are used. The number of fatali-
   ties resulting from such an assault is
   estimated as between twenty-five and forty
   million. The international medical pro-
   fession is concerned about these consequences mainly because physicians are now
   being asked to assist in the planning for
   the aftermath of a nuclear war. Despite
   the conflicting predictions of the official
   government sources and the private scientific studies, the conclusion of the group
   remains the same--the nation's health
   officials and practitioners could not
   handle the casualties from just a one
   megaton attack.

36.   Berger, John J. NUCLEAR POWER--THE
            UNVIABLE OPTION: A CRITICAL LOOK AT OUR
            ENERGY ALTERNATIVES. Introduction by
            Linus Pauling. Palo Alto, CA: Ramparts,
            1976.

        Beginning with the ABCs of reactor
technology, this book progresses through
discussions of the spiraling costs of
nuclear power, the radioactive garbage it
leaves behind, and the generally known
risks involved. The impetus of the work
is, however, to provide viable alternatives
to nuclear power. These other sources of
power include solar power, wind, geothermal,
ocean and tidal power as well as coal
gasification. The solution offered is that
only a citizen's movement can halt the
government supported nuclear growth in
favor of the many alternatives.

37.   Briggs, Raymond. WHEN THE WIND BLOWS.
            New York: Schocken Books, 1982.

        In a whimsical, cartoon format this
scenario reveals an elderly English
couple who have just heard of an impending
nuclear attack. Like trained poodles they
follow the vague governmental guidelines
for survival and only live through the
first 48 hours of the attack. The inner-
most thoughts, musings, and questions
raised by this simple, peasant couple
provide much food for thought. This is a
most gruesome, humorous book with an
adult message.

38.   Burleson, Clyde W. THE DAY THE BOMB FELL
            ON AMERICA: TRUE STORIES OF THE
            NUCLEAR AGE. Englewood Cliffs, NJ:
            Prentice-Hall, 1978.

        This collection of documented stories
        recounts some bizarre accidents or near-
        accidents involving nuclear or atomic
        weaponry worldwide. Most of the stories
        first appeared in the newspapers and were
        quickly discredited by U.S. and foreign
        governments as not being critical or in
        some cases, not ever occurring. Using
        these incidents as a backdrop the author
        demonstrates why we have the right to dis-
        trust nuclear power. Included are details
        of Soviet atomic disasters, the Karen
        Silkwood incident, and the invasion of a
        U.S. citizen's rights by a nuclear energy
        organization. The author offers a sane
        approach for coping with atomic energy, a
        power source which he realizes is probably
        here to stay.

39.   Caldicott, Helen. NUCLEAR MADNESS: WHAT
            YOU CAN DO! Brookline, MA: Autumn
            Press, 1978.

        This pediatrician turned nuclear acti-
        vist believes that life on our planet will
        become extinct if the progress of nuclear
        technology is not halted. Everything
        around us will become contaminated thus
        threatening the lives of everyone if radio-
        active pollutants remain unchecked. Dr.
        Caldicott makes an emotional plea for all
        individuals to become involved in the
        campaign to eliminate nuclear power. The
        U.S. cannot trust its elected officials to
        do the job because most of them have no
        sense of moral responsibility for humanity's
        future and their desire for re-election
        influences their decisions. Each citizen
        needs to be his own committee of one and
        help to avert M.A.D.ness--Mutually
        Assured Destruction.

40.   Clayton, Bruce D.   LIFE AFTER DOOMSDAY.
          Boulder, CO: Paladin, 1980.

          This is a survivalist book which
       provides step-by-step plans for living
       through a nuclear war.   Information about
       shelters, food storage, home medical
       techniques, and the psychology of survival
       are given.   The author informs you of the
       prime target areas of the U.S. as well as
       those least likely to be hit.   This is a
       most comprehensive work on survival which
       would be useful to follow through any
       major natural or man-made disaster.

41.   Committee for the Compilation of Materials
          on Damage Caused By the Atomic Bombs
          in Hiroshima and Nagasaki.   HIROSHIMA
          AND NAGASAKI: THE PHYSICAL, MEDICAL
          AND SOCIAL EFFECTS OF THE ATOMIC
          BOMBINGS.   Trans. by Eisei Ishikawa
          and David Swain.   New York: Basic,
          1981.

          As a large, photographic essay book
       Hiroshima and Nagasaki makes a powerful
       statement against the power and destruction
       potential of a nuclear attack.   The Japan-
       ese have prepared this book as a historical
       account of everything related to atomic
       bombs and as a graphic presentation of the
       first, and hopefully the last, bombs of
       this type.   Medical documents report that
       the first case of leukemia appeared as
       early as 1945 and that an atom bomb induced
       cataract was treated in 1948.   Various
       cancers of the thyroid, breasts, and lungs
       also increased after the war.   As yet no
       harmful genetic effects have been observed
       but an on-going generation by generation
       study is still being conducted.   The topic
       of psychological stress is touched upon
       and as one scarred and burned victim puts
       it "Unless you are an A-bomb victim you
       can't understand."   The survivors of the

attack suffer greatly and they feel that
the Japanese government refused to assist
them and even to this day, ignores them.
It has rejected the demand for an A-bomb
Victims Relief Law that would provide aid
to those who suffered bodily injury or loss
of livelihood. To the residents of these
two cities the Emperor's surrender within
ten days of the bombings was more shocking
than the attack itself as this made them
feel completely abandoned and rejected.
This massive volume provides a sombre look
at the living dead of Hiroshima and Nagasaki.

42.   COUNTDOWN TO A NUCLEAR MORATORIUM.
        Richard Munson, ed. Washington, DC:
        Environmental Action Foundation, 1976.

        Nuclear power is far too costly in
terms of the money spent, the environment
wasted, and the safety hazards which exist.
This is the primary thesis of this book of
fourteen essays written by well-known
anti-nuclear scholars, environmentalists,
doctors, and politicians. Coverage
includes the Browns Ferry incident, nuclear
safety, alternatives to nuclear power, and
the case for a nuclear moratorium. In
1979, after Three Mile Island, an expanded
version of this book was published under
the title *Accidents Will Happen: The Case
Against Nuclear Power*. (Item number 49)

43.   Cox, Arthur M.   RUSSIAN ROULETTE: THE
        SUPERPOWER GAME. New York: Times
        Books, 1982.

        With present day sophisticated computer
systems set to launch nuclear missiles on
warning, our survival can no longer be
assured. We have previously survived false
alarms--the risk now is that we could be
annihilated by accidental nuclear war. Cox
places the blame on the hawks in Moscow and
Washington. This work shows how the
policies of the two countries reinforce
that of each other. To avoid annihilation,
negotiation is necessary. Cox presents a
proposal for a two-track negotiated solution.
One solution bans direct or indirect military intervention by Third World superpowers
and the second is based on an agreement to
end the nuclear arms race. Cox draws upon
his extensive background in diplomacy,
intelligence, and arms control to suggest
how we may be able to divert this disastrous
course. A Soviet commentary is provided by
Georgy Arbatov, the foremost Soviet expert
on the U.S. and a close advisor to
President Reagan.

44.   Croall, Stephen. THE ANTI-NUCLEAR HANDBOOK.
        New York: Pantheon, 1978.

        Here is a most unusual comic book style
of documentary which warns against construc-
ting nuclear power plants, nuclear waste
dumps, of possible sabotage, and the
potential for accidents. Some historical
figures are brought to life in vignettes in
which their original words have been re-
written to reflect nuclear energy messages.
Most all of the points of the nuclear
controversy are included in this book but
their presence is masked by the cartoons.

45.   Curtis, Richard, and Elizabeth Hogan.
NUCLEAR LESSONS: AN EXAMINATION OF
NUCLEAR POWER'S SAFETY, ECONOMIC, AND
POLITICAL RECORD. Harrisburg, PA:
Stackpole, 1979.

     Portions of this book appeared under
the title *The Perils of the Peaceful Atom:*
The Myth of Safe Nuclear Power Plants.
published in 1969. This work points out
the fact that some of the authors' predictions came true with Three Mile Island.
The authors provide a thirty-year history
of nuclear lessons and reiterate their
beliefs that there are more practical and
safe alternatives to the energy question
than nuclear power.

46.   _____. THE PERILS OF THE PEACEFUL ATOM:
THE MYTH OF SAFE NUCLEAR POWER PLANTS.
New York: Ballantine, 1969.

     The authors attempt to bring together
in one source the facts and figures which
will alert U.S. citizens to the risks,
problems, and errors of nuclear power.
In their plea for a re-examination of our
peaceful nuclear program they argue that
the safety of every industry is now hanging
on that of the nuclear industry and warn
that commercial atomic power is an
unpromising investment. Utilizing the
scare tactic technique, the authors cover
the full gamut of the nuclear question,
cite hundreds of cases and experts, and
provide readers with their predictions
of the future of nuclear generated power.

47.   Drinian, Robert F. BEYOND THE NUCLEAR
         FREEZE. New York: Seabury, 1983.

         In this brief, simple book Father
    Drinian touches upon the topics of weapons
    proliferation and government policy. As a
    former congressman and law school professor
    he lends a welcomed insight to the politics
    of nuclear power and as a religious leader
    he displays his moral concerns. The book
    follows the growing anti-nuclear movement,
    the efforts to negotiate a nuclear mora-
    torium, and discusses freeze strategies.
    Father Drinian concludes that due to its
    global position and foreign policy, the U.S.
    will remain a nuclear power, but that
    activist citizen's groups can still strive
    to remove the threat of nuclear annihila-
    tion.

48.   Dunn, Lewis A. CONTROLLING THE BOMB:
         NUCLEAR PROLIFERATION IN THE 1980s.
         New Haven, CT: Yale University Press,
         1982.

         Dunn desires to slow the spread of
    nuclear know-how and weapons but does not
    believe that further proliferation will
    have beneficial effects. Pointing a finger
    at the strife in the Middle East, he
    wonders what the situation would be (or
    have been) if Israel, Syria, Pakistan and
    others possessed nuclear warfare. Either
    by theft, sabotage, outright purchase or by
    their own technological expertise, Dunn
    predicts that other countries will be able
    to enter the now elite nuclear club. He
    attacks the misconception that the presence
    of nuclear weapons may bring peace and
    stability to the Middle East by establishing
    regional deterrants much like that which
    prevented a US-USSR war. The latter half
    of *Controlling the Bomb* discusses a range
    of alternatives for a U.S. anti-prolifera-
    tion strategy. Dunn believes that the U.S.

should re-establish itself as a reliable
supplier of nuclear fuel, take aim to close
the technology export loopholes, impose
military and diplomatic sanctions on proliferation firebreaks as he calls them,
behind which nations could be held by the
threat of sanctions. This is an in-depth
political and diplomatic study of the
nuclear question which will be appreciated
by the knowledgeable layperson.

49.   Environmental Action Foundation. ACCIDENTS
       WILL HAPPEN: THE CASE AGAINST NUCLEAR
       POWER. Introduction by Ralph Nader.
       New York: Perennial/Harper, 1979.

       Here is a collection of essays from a
cross-section of America including senators,
doctors, lawyers, and enraged citizens who
lash out against the nuclear industry.
Topics covered include a history of radioactive wastes, long-term effects of radiation, and discussions of what happened at
Browns Ferry and Three Mile Island. These
are sincere and well-written essays. This
book is an expanded version of the 1976
title *Countdown to a Nuclear Moratorium*.
(Item number 42)

50.   Faulkner, Peter, ed.   THE SILENT BOMB: A
          GUIDE TO THE NUCLEAR ENERGY CONTROVERSY.
          New York: Random, 1977.

          Nuclear power represents the greatest
       single threat to the health and safety of
       humanity. This is the overriding premise
       of this powerful guide to the atomic
       industrial complex. Numerous accusations
       of U.S. government and business involvement
       in uranium price fixing, the placing of
       pro-nuclear people in key government posi-
       tions, and the concealment of studies
       whose results showed the nuclear risks are
       spelled out. The major portion of the book
       is comprised of excerpts from previously
       published books and articles written by
       well-known people, some of whom are
       represented elsewhere in this bibliography.

51.   THE FINAL EPIDEMIC: PHYSICIANS AND
          SCIENTISTS ON NUCLEAR WAR. Ruth Adams,
          and Susan Cullen, eds. Chicago: Educa-
          tional Foundation for Nuclear Science,
          1981.

          Twenty-two writers contribute essays to
       this book which recognizes the emergence of
       a new militarism in American thought.
       Exaggerated fears of the Soviet
       Union in recent years are to blame for our
       reckless foreign policy and provide the
       impetus for these comments by leading
       scientists and doctors. Coverage includes
       assessments of burn casualties, diseases,
       radioactive fallout, and cancer in atomic
       bomb survivors. The book closes with
       suggestions for preventing nuclear war and
       a statement by the International Physicians
       for the Prevention of Nuclear War.

52.   Ford, Daniel. BEYOND THE FREEZE: THE ROAD
          TO NUCLEAR SANITY. Boston: Beacon, 1982.

       The issue of a nuclear freeze is a simple,
    uncomplicated notion: "the United States
    and the Soviet Union should agree to a dead
    halt in all aspects of the nuclear arms
    race." This also entails the cessation of
    further nuclear testing of any nature. This
    proposal is discussed in great detail and
    attempts are made to answer many pressing
    questions. Excellent analyses are made as
    to the key developments in nuclear arms,
    the build-up of nuclear weaponry by the U.S.,
    and a review of the pros and cons of the
    freeze proposal.

53.   _____. THE CULT OF THE ATOM: THE SECRET
          PAPERS OF THE ATOMIC ENERGY COMMISSION.
       New York: Simon and Schuster, 1982.

       Mr. Ford is a former executive director
    of the Union of Concerned Scientists, a
    well-known anti-nuclear lobby group. He
    contends that the Atomic Energy Commission
    is guilty of a cover-up with regard to
    nuclear safety in the U.S. To prove his
    point the author took advantage of the
    Freedom of Information Act and read hundreds
    of AEC "secret" reports. The Emergency Core
    Cooling System (ECCS) hearings of 1971-72
    and the Reactor Safety Study of 1975 are
    extensively covered. Ford recommends up-
    grading the safety of existing plants and
    even suggests that the operation of some
    located in heavily populated areas be cur-
    tailed. His arguments add powerful fuel to
    the popular and political anti-nuclear
    forces. In general, this work attacks
    federal programs and agencies, the practice
    of poor site selection, and of course, the
    individuals surrounding the controversy.

54.   _____. THREE-MILE ISLAND: THIRTY MINUTES
              TO MELTDOWN. New York: Viking, 1982.

           An overview of the TMI accident and an
      explanation of why this is considered to
      have been a "Class 9" accident are provided
      for readers. The author sees some value
      in the incident in that it provided a good
      test case for all to study as well as
      having been an exercise in crisis manage-
      ment. Also covered are the NRC's plans for
      self-improvement and an analysis of its
      policies regarding nuclear safety. Some
      serious problems still exist with NRC
      reports and paperwork. Answers to
      questions raised by a presidential commis-
      sion established to look into the TMI
      incident have been suppressed by the Carter
      and Reagan administrations. Speculations
      as to why this occurred are offered.

55.   Fuller, John Grant. WE ALMOST LOST DETROIT.
              New York: Reader's Digest, 1975.

           Beginning with tales about the accident
      at Fermi No. 1 liquid metal fast-breeder
      reactor (LMFBR) in Lagoona Beach, Michigan
      in 1966, the author dramatically unfolds
      the safety issues surrounding nuclear
      reactor technology. Numerous other acci-
      dents or near-accidents not generally
      known to the public are also explained.
      The primary thrust of the book is to reveal
      the dangers of nuclear power and the fact
      that the public was misled by the former
      Atomic Energy Commission into thinking that
      nuclear energy is safe. The author con-
      tends that the AEC was so frightened by
      the estimated consequences of an accident
      that the members did not want to reveal
      them to the public. This is a fascinating
      book whose findings and arguments can help
      the cause of the anti-nuclear movement.

56. Gofman, John W. "IRREVY": AN IRREVERENT, ILLUSTRATED VIEW OF NUCLEAR POWER: A COLLECTION OF TALKS, FROM BLUNDERLAND TO SEABROOK IV. San Francisco: Committee for Nuclear Responsibility, 1979.

This is one of the more humorous and satirical books in the nuclear genre. Using cartoons to illustrate his points and issues, Dr. Gofman puts into print nine of his speeches given between 1975 and 1978 on the virtues of life without nuclear power. Numerous facts and figures are provided to lend some credibility to the cartoons.

57. _____, and Arthur R. Tamplin. POISONED POWER: THE CASE AGAINST NUCLEAR POWER BEFORE AND AFTER THREE MILE ISLAND. Emmaus, PA: Rodale, 1979.

In 1971, eight years before the Three Mile Island incident, these two authors predicted this near-disaster in a book entitled *Nuclear Power*. This revised and much expanded edition of that book revolves around the TMI affair. Great concern is still expressed for the health of future generations, the cover-ups which are commonplace in the government and the nuclear industry, and the controversial, utility-protecting Price-Anderson Act of 1957. In arguing that nuclear power is not necessary to produce electricity since today nuclear power only supplies 3½% of our total energy needs, the authors speak in favor of the alternative sources of energy. The book has many useful charts, diagrams, and statistics to support its arguments against nuclear power.

58.   Goodwin, Peter. NUCLEAR WAR: THE FACTS ON
           OUR SURVIVAL. New York: Rutledge,
           1981.

       Nuclear War provides readers with an
       insight into how the quest for atomic
       energy has resulted in a massive stockpile
       of nuclear bombs worldwide. Goodwin
       clearly explains nuclear power and shows
       who has it and who is most likely to use
       it in case of war. Coverage is provided
       which shows how nuclear radiation affects
       our environment and people. A unique chap-
       ter in this book is devoted to the pros
       and cons of evacuation, home modification,
       building and shelter types, and what
       supplies should be maintained in storage
       for survival purposes. This easy-to-read,
       well-illustrated book is a plea for reason
       and understanding that anything which
       lessens the danger of war is good.

59.   GRASSROOTS: AN ANTI-NUKE SOURCE BOOK.
           Fred Wilcox, ed. Trumansburg, NY:
           Crossing, 1980.

       Fifty-six very brief articles comprise
       this guide to protesting against nuclear
       power in very radical ways. Included is a
       checklist for demonstrators, a guide on
       how to use civil disobedience to obstruct
       nuclear power, tips on how to defend your-
       self without a lawyer, how to petition,
       and a variety of other ingenious plans.
       This "how to" book also has extensive lists
       of people, organizations, and newsletters
       to which you can turn for support and
       information. For financial assistance a
       list of foundations which grant money to
       combat the spread of nuclear power is most
       helpful.

60.   Gyorgy, Anna and Friends. NO NUKES:
      EVERYONE'S GUIDE TO NUCLEAR POWER.
      Boston: South End, 1979.

      Numerous experts worldwide have con-
      tributed to make *No Nukes* one of the better
      books of the anti-nuclear genre. It really
      is a guidebook leading the reader from a
      history of atomic development to the
      complex economics to the alternative
      sources of energy with which we should
      learn to live. Two revealing chapters
      examine the nuclear power structure and
      the existence of planned development of
      nuclear power in foreign countries. The
      book has many useful statistics, thorough
      and extensive references, and exceptional
      photos and drawings. This is another
      good "first book" on nuclear power.

61.   International Physicians for the Prevention
      of Nuclear War. LAST AID: THE MEDICAL
      DIMENSIONS OF NUCLEAR WAR. (Papers
      from a Congress) Eric Chivian, ed.
      San Francisco: Freeman, 1982.

      Seventy-two physicians from twelve
      countries attended the First Congress of
      the International Physicians for the Pre-
      vention of Nuclear War during which time
      they discussed how they may help to
      decrease the costs of the arms race (eco-
      nomic, moral, and psychological) by speak-
      ing out against nuclear war. The president
      of the group, Barnard Lown, states that
      world arms spending is around $1.4 billion
      per day, or $1 million per minute. He
      argues that a diversion of just three weeks
      of these funds, or about $30 billion, could
      provide a sanitary water supply for the
      entire world. Not only physicians, but all
      people should be concerned with the
      enormous spending for nuclear arms and try
      to persuade world leadership to spend money

to save lives, not to destroy them. In the
summary readers are reminded that "the
genocidal nature of nuclear weapons has
rendered nuclear war obsolete as a viable
means for resolving conflict....Wars begin
in the mind, but the mind is also capable
of preventing war."

62.   Jungk, Robert. THE NEW TYRANNY: HOW
          NUCLEAR POWER ENSLAVES US. New York:
          Grosset & Dunlap, 1979.

          Originally published in Germany in 1977,
this book has been credited with having a
major role in the banning of nuclear energy
in Austria and possibly Switzerland. It
has also fueled the fire of the nuclear
controversy in France, Germany, and Sweden.
Jungk logically explains that by following
the path of nuclear power we will be forced
to surrender some liberties one at a time
until we are finally part of a regimented
society. The book is complete with a
record of nuclear accidents and failures,
discussions of the proliferation and
terrorism questions, and the role of politics in this global concern for nuclear
power.

63.   Kaplan, Fred. THE WIZARDS OF ARMAGEDDON.
          New York: Simon & Schuster, 1983.

          Many writers, activists, and research-
ers have taken advantage of the recently
declassified government documents to
investigate the nuclear question. Journal-
ist Kaplan did just this to prepare a
historical development of nuclear weapons
policy since World War II. The book also
serves as a mini-biography of the chief
nuclear scientists of the time period and
reveals life as it was inside the labora-

tories which were cloaked in secrecy for nearly three decades. Briefly considered is the Reagan administration's policy and views toward nuclear power and nuclear war. Kaplan believes that President Reagan supports limited nuclear war fighting but adds that nobody in the administration has ever asked how a nuclear war might be fought. The author thinks that the question should be asked and that the various alternatives should be studied.

64.   Katz, Arthur M. LIFE AFTER NUCLEAR WAR: THE ECONOMIC AND SOCIAL IMPACTS OF NUCLEAR ATTACKS ON THE UNITED STATES. Cambridge, MA: Ballinger, 1982.

This lengthy book takes issue with the terms "acceptable" and "unacceptable" damage as they pertain to measures of psychological destruction and survival after a nuclear weapons exchange. Katz informs readers that the amount of weapons required to create unacceptable damage is far smaller than we have been led to believe. Were key industrial facilities to be rendered inoperable by well-planned attacks, a modern industrial society would be seriously crippled. We are told that the social, political, and economic life would be so drastically altered in an attack that most of us would consider it to be unacceptable damage. Katz adds that all of this doesn't even take into consideration the possibility that even minimal key hits could prevent any type of biological survival. Katz also criticizes the high level crisis evacuation plans as useless. Instead of developing these plans, high government officials should be concerned with developing plans for a nuclear disarmament and a nuclear freeze.

65.   Langer, Victor, and Walter Thomas.
        THE NUCLEAR WAR FUN BOOK. New York:
        Holt, Rinehart and Winston, 1982.

        In a morbid, yet humorous manner, the
        authors present an illustrated book of fun
        and games to be enjoyed after a nuclear
        holocaust. As they state, "Just because
        you may be surrounded by destruction,
        doesn't mean you can't be creative."
        Included are post-nuclear war activities
        and a few pre-war games. Some can be
        played outdoors after the radiation level
        has dropped (Radioactive Tag) and others
        must be played in the fallout shelter
        (Connect the Craters and Backgamma Ray).
        This is definitely not a book you would read
        to your children at bedtime.

66.   Leppzer, Robert, ed. VOICES FROM THREE
        MILE ISLAND: THE PEOPLE SPEAK OUT.
        Trumansburg, NY: Crossing, 1980.

        Full of emotion, this small book
        includes testimonials from thirteen
        residents in the TMI accident area. In
        a folksy style we hear what each was doing
        when the accident occurred, their immediate
        thoughts, and how their lives have been
        affected since that March 1979 day. The
        worries, frustrations, and the anger of
        each resident is felt as you read these
        interviews. Most realize that there is a
        need for energy but now they think there
        may be safer ways to generate it than
        through nuclear power.

67.   Lovins, Amory B., and L. Hunter Lovins.
      ENERGY/WAR: BREAKING THE NUCLEAR LINK.
      San Francisco: Friends of the Earth,
      1980.

      Nuclear power equals nuclear war as we
      are told in some very convincing arguments
      by the Lovinses. The U.S., and others with
      the atomic knowledge, had best not share
      this knowledge by educating foreign
      students in our universities. We are
      reminded that nuclear power is not a sig-
      nificant substitute for oil. Nuclear
      power only generates electricity which
      amounts to one-tenth of the U.S. power
      needs. Oil, on the other hand, has numer-
      ous household and industrial uses. The
      authors provide their plans for saving oil
      and offer some advice for Detroit auto-
      makers. This is not an elementary book on
      the nuclear power issue but, nevertheless,
      the writings of this well-known husband and
      wife anti-nuclear team will be appreciated
      by the well-informed reader.

68.   Nader, Ralph, and John Abbotts. THE MENACE
      OF ATOMIC ENERGY. New York: Norton,
      1977.

      In a manner of writing that only he can
      get away with, Ralph Nader takes on the
      nuclear power industry, its scientists,
      the governmental agencies, and the
      utilities which support and manufacture
      reactor technology. Pointing to the fact
      that nuclear engineers have resigned due to
      the defects and deficiencies in the nuclear
      industry and the regulatory agencies, Nader
      surmises that the reactor industry is
      crumbling technically and economically.
      Mr. Nader vehemently exclaims that atomic
      fission is unsafe, unnecessary, and an
      economic folly in this controversial book.

69.   Neild, Robert. HOW TO MAKE UP YOUR MIND
            ABOUT THE BOMB. London: Deutsch, 1981.

            This Cambridge University Professor of
        Economics uses this small book to
        contribute to the British policy debate
        regarding American nuclear presence in
        Great Britain. He contends that Britons
        are more threatened than strengthened by
        American nuclear bases and further adds
        that Britain may not need them. The United
        States can be relied upon to defend its
        investments and role in Europe but the
        presence of nuclear weapons on British soil
        adds to the risk that Britain will be
        subject to a nuclear attack. Neild notes
        that U.S. assistance to the British nuclear
        weapons program has had two conditions:
        that British forces be assigned to NATO and
        that Britain continues to provide the U.S.
        with military facilities. Fervent in his
        displeasure with this agreement he calls
        for a public debate about U.S. military
        bases in Britain, asks where the nuclear
        arms race is going, and sees dangers in
        superpower arms control negotiations.
        Neild wants Britain to become self-reliant
        in matters of defense like the French, but
        without nuclear weapons. With this book
        the author makes frequent attacks on the
        reckless American foreign policy.
        Although this is geared to British reader-
        ship, Americans will find it useful as a
        history of U.S. nuclear involvement over-
        seas and as a guide to understanding the
        strategic importance of European military
        bases.

70.   Nelkin, Dorothy, and Michael Pollak.
            THE ATOM BESIEGED: ANTI-NUCLEAR
            MOVEMENTS IN FRANCE & GERMANY.
            Cambridge, MA: MIT Press, 1982.

            Focusing on the problems in western
        Europe, Nelkin and Pollak provide a

comparative analysis of nuclear opposition
in France and Germany. Recent explosive
and emotional attacks have been made in
both countries by the anti-nuclear movement.
A history of the movement and the valuable
governmental responses provides us with an
understanding of the nuclear opposition and
a look at the political processes of two
European countries. This is not a book
for the novice nuclear reader but rather
it is directed to the well-informed
individual.

71.   NUCLEAR WAR: WHAT'S IN IT FOR YOU?
        New York: Pocket Books, 1982.

        Ground Zero is the Washington, DC
based group responsible for putting
together this book of nuclear war advice.
The group is a nonpartisan educational
organization dedicated to supplying information which the public has a right to
know. The book covers the immediate
effects of nuclear war and what to do if
you do manage to survive a nuclear
exchange. A scouting report on the
Russians, a game of twenty questions about
nuclear war, and the weapons proliferation
problem round out the book.

72.   O'Keefe, Bernard J. THE NUCLEAR
         HOSTAGES. Boston: Houghton Mifflin,
         1983.

         Having worked with Robert Oppenheimer
    on the first atomic bomb, Mr. O'Keefe
    lends his privileged insight into global
    discussions on the nuclear advances since
    World War II to the general public. He
    provides an excellent history of fission
    research and of the Los Alamos Laborator-
    ies. This author is one of the growing
    number of scientists who formerly made
    their living in the nuclear industry and
    who have now turned against it. Among his
    warnings he attacks the treaty process as
    being ineffective in stopping the arms
    race. O'Keefe has his own survival plan
    which he is willing to share--"Stay home,
    take two aspirins, and hope for the best."
    The hostages referred to in the title are
    the Russian and American citizens who are
    held hostage to each other. According to
    the author we are held hostage to the
    mutual strategies of deterrence or
    mutually assured destruction.

73.   Olson, McKinley C. UNACCEPTABLE RISK: THE
         NUCLEAR POWER CONTROVERSY. New York:
         Bantam, 1976.

         The "technological monster", nuclear
    fission power, is once again on trial in
    this book which warns that nuclear power
    is a threat to the future of life on this
    planet. Four major concerns prevail
    throughout the text: 1) radioactive waste;
    2) the unexplored relationship between
    radioactivity, disease, and genetic defects;
    3) the dangers of error, sabotage, acci-
    dents, and theft; and 4) the question of
    a worldwide proliferation of nuclear
    weapons. A careful analysis is given to
    numerous nuclear plants and to the contro-
    versial roots of nuclear power. Many

examples of what citizens have done to
prevent nuclear power from entering their
neighborhoods and some predictions on what
the future will bring are also provided.
A nationwide list of nuclear plants, their
capacity, ownership, and operation date
is most useful.

74. Peterson, Jeannie, and Don Hinrichsen, eds.
     NUCLEAR WAR: THE AFTERMATH. New York:
     Pergamon, 1982.

     This collection of fourteen articles
first appeared as a special issue of the
international journal, *Ambio*. The book
was published in the belief that knowledge
of the consequences of a nuclear war may
serve as a deterrent to such an event.
This is a very scientific, easy-to-read
appraisal of the effects of a global war
based not on the worst possible war, nor
even a "limited war," but one based on
the premise that once a nuclear war
breaks out it would probably be neither
containable nor controllable.

75.   Pollard, Robert, ed. THE NUGGET FILE.
        Cambridge, MA: Union of Concerned
        Scientists, 1979.

        The Freedom of Information Act
        allowed the Union of Concerned Scientists
        access to public Nuclear Regulatory
        Commission documents, one of which was
        "The Nugget File." This file was a
        special, internal file maintained by
        Dr. Stephen H. Hanauer, a senior NRC
        official, for over ten years. The file
        identifies serious accidents and safety
        deficiencies at U.S. nuclear power plants
        in very revealing, but brief, reports.
        Included are such deficiency reports as
        "Emergency Core Cooling System Inopera-
        tive-Valves in Wrong Position", "Loss of
        Control of Reactor Water Level-Blown Fuse",
        "Reactor Water Flow Obstruction-Plywood
        Left in Emergency Cooling Pipe" and many
        more. The Nugget File is too large to be
        published in its entirety so this book of
        abstracts provides researchers with an
        adequate summary and appropriate citations
        to the actual source should a more in-depth
        reading be necessary.

76.   Pringle, Peter, and James Spigelman.
        THE NUCLEAR BARONS. New York: Holt,
        Rinehart and Winston, 1981.

        In this lengthy book the secrets of
        the nuclear barons, the scientific elite
        who controlled the growth of the nuclear
        industry for over four decades, are
        revealed. This international study in
        radiation hazards, waste disposal, plant
        safety, and weapons proliferation provides
        much for the reader to ponder. The role
        of the British, French, and Indian govern-
        ments are chronicled as they pertain to

the development of nuclear power. The
authors do not advocate the shutdown of
all nuclear power plants in all nations
for they do realize that some nations may
have no practical alternative due to the
availability of resources. They do agree
that although nuclear power may be
necessary, its use should be kept to a
minimum. It is hoped that the information
in this book will help to bring about a
much needed change in the industry.

77.   PROTEST AND SURVIVE. E.P. Thompson, and
          Dan Smith, eds. New York: Monthly
          Review, 1981. Introduction by Daniel
          Ellsberg.

       As the American version of a British
book with the same title, this work has
ten contributed essays. It provides a
purely British and European view of
American nuclear policy and international
diplomacy. Europeans fear that the U.S.
and Russia are going to "fight it out"
and that Europe will be the stage for the
battle. The dangers of a nuclear war and
an unlimited arms race must be discussed
openly. The lengthy Ellsberg introduction
"Call to Mutiny" is by itself worth
reading and *if* what he says is true, then
we should prepare for World War III.

78.   Rapoport, Roger.   THE GREAT AMERICAN
               BOMB MACHINE. New York: Dutton, 1971.

               In a tongue-in-cheek manner, Mr.
           Rapoport takes exception to the entire
           nuclear defense system of the U.S.   He
           attacks the lack of common sense in the
           deployment of antimissiles, the irony of
           SALT and AEC weapons production programs,
           and such popular tourist attractions as
           the Sandia nuclear bomb museum run by the
           Department of Defense. The solution to
           a safe and guaranteed future includes the
           dismantling of the weapons program and
           the great American bomb machine should be
           declared a public health hazard. Rapoport
           argues that Dr. Glenn Seaborg, the AEC
           chairman at the time, should have resigned
           and the author abhors the fact that
           Seaborg was paid $100,000 in 1955 by the
           U.S. government for the fine job he did
           on the plutonium separative process used
           to make the Nagasaki bomb. Although some
           of the material is dated, we are still
           involved in SALT and weapons have once
           again become a political question.

79.   Scheer, Robert.   WITH ENOUGH SHOVELS:
               REAGAN, BUSH AND NUCLEAR WAR. New
               York: Random House, 1982.

               This *Los Angeles Times* reporter has
           discovered a reversal in the longstanding
           American assumption that nuclear war means
           mutual suicide. Now the prevailing
           thought is that American leaders have
           chosen to fight and win in a nuclear war.
           The leaders also expect that once the war
           is won that the U.S. will return to
           normal. The leaders believe that we are
           living in a pre-war and not a post-war
           world. The Soviets are bent on world
           conquest and the only way in which the

U.S. can meet this challenge is with the
determination to shrink the Soviet empire
and to alter Soviet society. Scheer
discovered Reagan's secret plan in a report
called the National Security Decision
Document which commits President Reagan to
the idea that a global nuclear war can be
won. Scheer exposes the deadly course of
the U.S. in this book which was written by
means of exclusive interviews with President
Reagan and several of his key staff and
cabinet.

80.   Schell, Jonathan. THE FATE OF THE EARTH.
       New York: Knopf, 1982.

       The Fate of the Earth is a published
collection of articles which originally
appeared in *The New Yorker*. Schell
discusses his concept of the "nuclear
predicament" as people's indifference or
apathy to the threat inherent in the
nuclear arsenals. The world, on the whole,
just doesn't think about them very much.
Schell would like to change this attitude
and attempts to do so by providing an
account of what the nuclear holocaust
might be like. He is probably very
accurate in his belief that the human life
would be extinguished or life on Earth
would be impossible due to the loss of the
ozone layer. One of the author's scenarios
depicts what would happen if a one
megaton bomb was dropped above the Empire
State Building. The conclusion to this
dramatic work is a chapter called "The
Second Death", the theme of which is that
worse than being killed is that the whole
species might be eliminated. Schell also
contrasts the notions of death and extinction, the doctrine of deterrence, and
political solutions in his closing remarks.

81.   SHUT DOWN: NUCLEAR POWER ON TRIAL.
         Summertown, TN: The Book Pub. Co.,
         1979.

         Shut Down is the transcript of the
         court testimony of two noted nuclear
         activists as they spoke at the October 2,
         1978 Federal Court hearing for the case
         Jeannine Honiker vs. Joseph M. Hendrie
         et al in Nashville, Tennessee. Mrs.
         Honiker's nineteen year old daughter con-
         tracted leukemia--the alleged cause of
         which was radiation from a nearby nuclear
         power plant. With the aid of Catfish
         Alliance and Farm Legal, a case against
         the Nuclear Regulatory Commission was
         prepared. The objective was to intervene
         in the licensing process of and to
         ultimately shutdown what was then the
         world's largest nuclear plant located in
         Hartsville, TN. The only point to be
         determined in this hearing was whether
         or not the judge had the jurisdiction to
         hear the case. On January 12, 1979 the
         case was dismissed for lack of that
         jurisdiction. Testimony in the hearing
         and the commentary following the tran-
         script are both vehement protests and
         emotional pleas to abandon nuclear power
         for the sake of our children and the
         future of this world.

82.   Sternglass, Ernest. SECRET FALLOUT: LOW-
         LEVEL RADIATION FROM HIROSHIMA TO
         THREE-MILE ISLAND. Rev. ed. New
         York: McGraw-Hill, 1981.

         Secret Fallout is an expanded version
         of the 1972 book by Dr. Sternglass
         entitled *Low-Level Radiation*. As in the
         earlier edition the author is still
         concerned with the health effects of low-
         level radiation and why the military, the
         nuclear industry, and some scientists

have tried to bury the facts. Using
examples from incidents at U.S. nuclear
power generating plants, the author
describes the effects that nuclear testing
and power plant radiation releases have
had, or will have, on the lives of the
people.

83.   Sweet, Colin, ed. THE FAST BREEDER
            REACTOR: NEED? COST? RISK?
            London: Macmillan, 1980.

        As the title implies, this work should
should analyze the pressing questions
of need, cost, and risk of fast breeder
reactors. In actuality it is a collection
of fourteen papers attacking FBRs and
nuclear power in general. Breeders were
originally designed to be a less expensive
manner of producing nuclear energy. The
only way to find out whether or not this
production is actually cheaper would be
to build large fast breeder reactors.
This work is very much against this type
of thinking and argues that radiation
hazards to the people may limit the
growth of nuclear power and that nuclear
energy and civil liberties are incompat-
ible. Other essays attempt to sway
readers to investigate more efficient
alternative sources like oil burning
heaters. Great concern is expressed for
the dangerous disposable wastes of the
fast breeder reactors. Finally, rather
than calling just for an end to FBRs,
this book calls for an end to all nuclear
power generation.

84.   Tamplin, Arthur R., and John W. Gofman.
        POPULATION CONTROL THROUGH NUCLEAR
        POLLUTION. Chicago: Nelson-Hall,
        1970.

        Two of the most knowledgeable anti-
        nuclear scientists attack the atomic
        industry with much fervor and emotion in
        this book. Citing criticism from within
        the nuclear industry and the fact that
        self-serving nuclear technology promoters
        are ignoring the known health hazards,
        both physicists call for a nuclear
        moratorium. Blind to all known good
        which has come from nuclear research, Drs.
        Gofman and Tamplin continue their crusade
        to halt the advancement of the industry.
        They freely use cynical phrases such as
        "Will your grandchild's genes be fit for
        your great-grandchildren to wear? " to
        make their points about radiation,
        pollution, and public health arrogance.
        This is a revealing easy-to-read book by
        two of the better known polemics in the
        campaign to thwart the growth of nuclear
        technology.

85.   Taylor, Theodore B., and Mason Willrich.
        NUCLEAR THEFT: RISKS AND SAFEGUARDS.
        Cambridge, MA: Ballinger, 1974.

        Starting off with a chapter on how
        to make nuclear weapons, the authors
        clearly make their point--anyone can
        obtain the formula through public, un-
        classified sources. Other sections of the
        book cover the U.S. safeguards against
        nuclear theft, the numerous types of
        nuclear theft risks and an abundance of
        recommendations which the Atomic Energy
        Commission, now the Nuclear Regulatory
        Commission, should consider. Useful
        tables and charts reflecting the growth
        of nuclear power complement the text.

86.   TO AVOID A CATASTROPHE: A STUDY IN FUTURE
            NUCLEAR WEAPONS POLICY. Michael P.
            Hamilton, ed. Grand Rapids, MI:
            Eerdmans, 1977.

            Twelve essays comprise this anthology
    of nuclear gloom and doom. A prevailing
    concern is that the proliferation of
    atomic weapons will continue and that a
    nuclear strike is inevitable. It is also
    hoped that such a strike will instill so
    much fear and concern in the people of
    this world that the aggressors, most
    likely the U.S. and/or Russia, will step
    back, look at what they have done, and
    take aim to ensure that it will not happen
    again. The topics of the papers include
    a history of the atomic age, a terrorist
    attack on a nuclear facility, sabotage,
    safety and security, and some practical
    steps toward disarmament.

87.   Touraine, Alain et al. ANTI-NUCLEAR
            PROTEST: THE OPPOSITION TO NUCLEAR
            ENERGY IN FRANCE. Trans. by Peter
            Fawcett. New York: Cambridge, 1983.

            The anti-nuclear movement in France is
    creating a new generation of educated and
    upperclass protestors and activists. This
    book is a study of several of those
    groups including industrial unionists,
    engineers, physicians, and housewives.
    Touraine and his social researchers
    arranged for several group discussions at
    which anti-nuclear individuals were
    gathered to speak with each other or to
    be challenged by others present who had
    opposing views. Discussions in the book
    between these diverse groups center
    around an idea exchange with the ultimate
    goal being the founding of a new social

movement within the anti-nuclear campaign.
This is exactly what Touraine and his
colleagues are trying to accomplish and
they try to direct these anti-nuclear
circles to more pragmatic forms of political action. The authors feel that these
groups are at the center of pending social
change and modernization. The thoughts of
many of those interviewed are fantasy-like,
making readers question the ideological
attitudes of these French citizens. This
is a superficial study that will provide
a minimal understanding of the French
resistance to nuclear growth.

88.   Union of Concerned Scientists. THE
       NUCLEAR FUEL CYCLE: A SURVEY OF THE
       PUBLIC HEALTH, ENVIRONMENTAL, AND
       NATIONAL SECURITY EFFECTS OF NUCLEAR
       POWER. Rev. ed. Cambridge, MA:
       MIT Press, 1975.

       A wide array of essays are included
in this volume of eight very separate and
independent articles surveying the effects
of nuclear power on society. Although
there is no cohesiveness between essays
the thought flow is manageable since they
are arranged in the order of the fuel
cycle. Essays track the uranium from the
mine through the manufacturing stages,
and then follows with the elements of
reactor operation, transportation of the
wastes, and finally the disposal of the
wastes. A few of the case studies are
quite detailed and contain many graphs and
tables. The Union of Concerned Scientists
is an advocate organization which studies
the impact of advanced technology on
society and this work will serve as a good
follow-up to a more basic text on nuclear
power.

89.   Williams, Frederick C., and David A.
            Deese, eds. NUCLEAR NONPROLIFERATION:
            THE SPENT FUEL PROBLEM. New York:
            Pergamon, 1980.

            The Spent Fuel Problem focuses on the
        by-product of the commercial nuclear
        fuel cycle and investigates what happens
        to fuel after it has been irradiated and
        withdrawn from the power reactors. One
        of the new questions which this problem
        brings forth is the issue of nuclear
        weapons proliferation resulting from
        exploited by-products. This series of
        papers discusses the problem of nuclear
        waste management as it relates to global
        security and the safeguards at nuclear
        installations. At present most spent fuel
        is being stored until the day when it can
        be economically used in fast breeder reac-
        tors--a day which may not come, according
        to the authors. Until this time, however,
        the spent fuel remains a radioactive
        nuisance. The editors provide the readers
        with some political options and venture
        some solutions to the nuclear by-product
        dilemma.

90.   Wohlstetter, Albert et al. SWORDS FROM
            PLOWSHARES: THE MILITARY POTENTIAL
            OF CIVILIAN NUCLEAR ENERGY. Chicago:
            University of Chicago Press, 1979.

            In the coming years many nations will
        be on the threshold of nuclear bomb
        production, including several countries
        which have agreed to abstain from such
        production. This book suggests that there
        is a need for a basic change in the rules
        governing the development and export of
        nuclear power, which does not necessarily
        call for a complete cessation of nuclear
        energy production. The author has made an

excellent analysis between the civil
nuclear technology which we need for
electric production and the military issue
of nuclear weaponry. This is a most fact-
ual, well-documented book.

91.   Zuckerman, Solly, Lord. NUCLEAR ILLUSION
          AND REALITY. New York: Viking, 1982.

       A British overview of the nuclear con-
troversy is presented by this one-time
Chief Scientific Advisor to the Minister
of Defense under Prime Minister Harold
Macmillan. The early U.S., UK, and USSR
involvement in the development and build-up
of nuclear warheads is traced. Lots of
"If a one-megaton bomb hit (city), x number
of people would be killed outright"
examples are provided. These are useful
if one needs to quote such destruction
projections. The illusion referred to in
the title is the idea that nuclear weapons
could ever be used as a means of defense.
He asserts that a nuclear war would be
total and mutually annihilating. Zuckerman
advocates a "no first use" policy and a
unilateral nuclear disarmament. His final
thesis is that "the existence of nuclear
weapons can neither prevent war nor
defend in war."

Neutral

92.   ACCIDENT AT THREE MILE ISLAND: THE HUMAN
DIMENSIONS. David L. Sills, C.P. Wolf,
and Vivien B. Shelanski, eds. Boulder,
CO: Westview, 1982.

This is the first real sociological
study of the impact of Three Mile Island.
Numerous experts have analyzed organizational behavior, the nuclear regulation
process, the public's involvement in
national decision making, and the conflict
and consensus process. The stress and
psychological effects of the TMI accident
on the residents of the area are still
being uncovered. Much scrutiny is given
to nationwide community attitudes toward
nuclear plants, nuclear responsibility,
and the human element in the operation of
nuclear power plants. These essays will
prove to be landmark assessments of the
sociological and psychological effects of
nuclear disasters.

93.   Bolt, Bruce A.   NUCLEAR EXPLOSIONS AND
        EARTHQUAKES: THE PARTED VEIL. New
        York: Freeman, 1976.

        The author presents an interesting
        query on a sensitive matter--how to dis-
        tinguish between earthquakes and under-
        ground nuclear tests which are forbidden
        by treaties. In very elementary terms
        Bolt provides the reader with summaries of
        the mechanics of nuclear devices and the
        elements of seismography. He also explains
        the use of nuclear devices in engineering
        and the environmental effects of under-
        ground tests. With this background the
        reader is challenged to study the earth-
        quake/nuclear test data and to decide for
        himself.

94.   Browne, Corrine, and Robert Munroe.
        TIME BOMB: UNDERSTANDING THE THREAT OF
        NUCLEAR POWER. New York: Morrow, 1981.

        Time Bomb is a beautiful, flowing story
        that reads like a PBS documentary on the
        atomic bomb. In this superbly researched
        book the Manhattan Project, the Trinity
        Test site, and the developments of the Los
        Alamos and Oak Ridge laboratories are
        traced from their very beginnings. Playing
        a major role is J. Robert Oppenheimer whose
        involvement was as the Manhattan Project
        Supervisor and procuror of the great
        scientific minds. The distrust of nuclear
        power by Dr. John Gofman, former medical
        physicist for Lawrence Livermore Laboratory
        and now an anti-nuclear activist, is
        captured in a brief vignette about his
        early involvement in the nuclear age. This
        work is one of the most readable histories
        of the atomic age which has no emotional
        attachments to either side of the issue.

95.   THE CALIFORNIA INITIATIVE: ANALYSIS AND
        DISCUSSION OF THE ISSUES. Palo Alto,
        CA: Stanford University Institute for
        Energy Studies, 1976.

        In June 1976 Californians cast their
        votes on the California Nuclear Initiative
        (Proposition 15), a decision that was to
        determine the fate of nuclear power in that
        state. The Initiative was sure to be a
        model for other states. This book is a
        collection of six essays intended to
        provide a balanced analysis and discussion
        of the nuclear issue in California for the
        voters. No position on the Initiative is
        taken, but rather the questions and/or
        benefits of waste, jobs, risks, nuclear
        power, alternative energies, and the
        future are examined. Concise and right to
        the point, this manual can serve as a guide
        for citizen action groups as well as
        legislators contemplating the nuclear power
        issue in their state.

96.   Chicken, John C. NUCLEAR POWER HAZARD
        CONTROL POLICY. New York: Pergamon,
        1982.

        This book is more of a history of
        public outcries and movements concerned
        with the hazards of nuclear power than a
        scholarly policy book as the title suggests.
        Chicken has clearly written a general
        account of how the perceived terrors of
        nuclear warfare have masked the real, but
        different, risks of the nuclear power
        industry. We are reminded that it has
        been safer to generate power from uranium
        than from coal or oil. Indepth coverage
        is given to the counterculture as a tool
        for protest. The history of protest is
        traced to the U.S. and is a response to

Vietnam resentment and the denial of
civil rights to minorities. The movement
gained momentum in Britain where there are
still very powerful anti-nuclear lobbies
who question the need for nuclear power and
who continue to criticize the site selection
procedure for specific reactors. A careful
and thorough analysis of the risk-related
decisions and the influence which public
interest groups has had on these decisions
is provided. Briefly mentionned are the
Browns Ferry accident and the controversial
Rasmussen Report. In a finale, Chicken
clarifies for the reader England's Windscale
Inquiry of 1978.

97.   Clarke, Donald, ed. ENERGY. New York:
          Arco, 1979.

     This basic history of energy provides
a firm background in the understanding
and development of nuclear energy. From
Newton to Oppenheimer and from the theory
of energy to solar power, Clarke outlines
the essentials of power production. The
latter portion of the book covers electro-
magnetics and nuclear energy. Numerous
drawings and photographs accompany this
text designed for the general reader.

98.   Cook, Constance.   NUCLEAR POWER AND LEGAL
           ADVOCACY: THE ENVIRONMENTALISTS AND THE
           COURTS. Lexington, MA: Heath, 1980.

       Here we have an attempt to record the
       actions of one type of anti-nuclear group
       and that of the legal process. Specifi-
       cally, the case of the Midland, Michigan
       nuclear power plant is followed through the
       court system. The Supreme Court did rule
       in favor of licensing and building the
       plant after several years of litigation.
       The roles of the Nuclear Regulatory Com-
       mission and the judiciary are examined
       very closely. A list of environmental
       activist groups and public interest groups
       involved in the Midland case as well as
       their activities is included.

99.   Deese, David A.   NUCLEAR POWER AND RADIO-
           ACTIVE WASTE. Lexington, MA: Lexington
           Books, 1978.

       Nuclear Power and Radioactive Waste
       focuses on the possibility of sub-seabed
       disposal of radioactive waste. Deese
       discusses the advantages and disadvantages
       of this controversial method of waste
       disposal and confronts the reader with
       many economic, ethical, legal, political,
       and social issues along the way. Also
       covered is a brief history of ocean dump-
       ing and the international laws and regula-
       tions concerned. The matter of interna-
       tional public acceptance of seabed disposal
       will be the first hurdle to pass for those
       supporting this avenue for radioactive
       waste disposal.

100.   Del Tredici, Robert. THE PEOPLE OF THREE
        MILE ISLAND. New York: Sierra Club,
        dist. by Scribners, 1980.

        Interviews with thirty-seven residents
        and officials about what happened at Three
        Mile Island comprise the core of this book.
        The remarks of the people reveal their
        fears, frustrations, and outright anger
        with the utility company and its officials.
        The overriding concern is that much of the
        truth was hidden from the residents. A
        detailed chronicle of the accident is
        included. This book is very similar to
        the book by Robert Leppzer, *Voices From
        Three Mile Island* (see item number 66) and
        even includes interviews with some of the
        same people.

101.   Ebbin, Stephen, and Raphael Kasper.
        CITIZEN GROUPS AND THE NUCLEAR POWER
        CONTROVERSY. Cambridge, MA: MIT
        Press, 1974.

        This useful study is a report of citizen
        input into the nuclear power plant siting
        controversy. It was found that ignorance,
        pessimism, and doom forecasting is common
        among activist groups. Citizens groups
        cause long and costly delays in the con-
        struction and licensing of nuclear power
        plants and these costs come right back to
        the public. The authors discovered that
        lip service to public interest groups is
        rampant all the while utilities are plot-
        ting under the bargaining table to move in
        the bulldozers. The role of the regulatory
        agencies in the licensing process is
        explained as one which merely sets stan-
        dards, criteria, and rules for construc-
        tion. A history of the first contested
        licesing case of 1956 is summarized as is
        the movement to resist nuclear power in
        general.

102.   Edelhertz, Herbert, and Marilyn Walsh.
        THE WHITE-COLLAR CHALLENGE TO NUCLEAR
        SAFEGUARDS. Lexington, MA: Heath, 1978.

        We have all been informed about the
        activists and terrorists who pose threats
        to nuclear safety but here the authors
        provide us with a relatively unexposed
        culprit--employees of nuclear installations
        who break the security systems for a price.
        Employee sabotage and the diversion of
        classified materials presents special prob-
        lems in nuclear security and safety. The
        authors point out that this area of sabo-
        tage is too often overlooked as the regu-
        latory agencies are primarily concerned
        with the external threats. As the nuclear
        materials market expands the diversion
        and sales of illicit materials becomes more
        profitable. *White-Collar Challenge*
        recommends a study of white collar crime
        in the nuclear industry and the formulation
        of safeguards designed to deter white
        collar crime in the atomic industry. The
        authors treat this topic as if this is a
        potential crime whereas in actuality such
        criminal activities have already been
        documented. Readers interested in this
        rarely written about topic will find this
        a stimulating book.

103.   Fenn, Scott. THE NUCLEAR POWER DEBATE:
        ISSUES AND CHOICES. New York: Praeger,
        1981.

        The nuclear industry continues to be
        plagued by economic, political, and tech-
        nological uncertainties. Many industry
        trends are brought to light including the
        observation that utility companies have
        begun a self-imposed moratorium on nuclear
        plant orders. Time is needed to plan and

study nuclear plant performance data. The
Nuclear Regulatory Commission, a once
strong advocate of nuclear power, has even
made decisions that have had an adverse
impact on the economic and political
acceptance of nuclear power. Regardless
of the neutrality of this book, the author
agrees that the international development
of nuclear power will aid in the proliferation of nuclear weapons.

104.   Fermi, Laura. ATOMS FOR THE WORLD: UNITED
        STATES PARTICIPATION IN THE CONFERENCE
        ON THE PEACEFUL USES OF ATOMIC ENERGY.
        Chicago: University of Chicago Press,
        1957.

        The author is the widow of Enrico Fermi
        and *Atoms for the World* is her story of
        the U.S. role at the 1955 International
        Conference on the Peaceful Uses of Atomic
        Energy held in Geneva, Switzerland. The
        book does not pretend to be the official
        recorded history of the conference but
        rather it is only one layperson's view and
        impressions of the proceedings. Covered
        in the summary are the Russian scientists
        in Geneva, the technical exhibits which she
        found to be fascinating, power, radiation
        hazards, and much more. This is an easy
        to comprehend encapsulation of the first
        conference of this type. Although this is
        not a recently published book, the signi-
        ficance of this conference and Laura
        Fermi's comments are historically signifi-
        cant.

105.   Francis, John, and Paul Abrecht, eds.
         FACING UP TO NUCLEAR POWER: RISKS AND
         POTENTIALITIES OF THE LARGE-SCALE USE
         OF NUCLEAR ENERGY. Philadelphia:
         Westminster, 1976.

         Written by leading experts this collec-
         tion of essays discusses the economic,
         ecological, and ethical issues of nuclear
         power. Predictions are made as to what we
         can expect by the year 2001 by way of
         nuclear energy. Included in this book is
         the renowned and controversial report of
         the "Ecumenical Hearing on Nuclear Energy"
         sponsored by the World Council of Churches
         held in Sweden in 1976. As is evident from
         the tone of many of the essays, the real
         debate over the future of nuclear energy
         has scarcely begun.

106.   Gompert, David C. et al. NUCLEAR WEAPONS
         AND WORLD POLITICS: ALTERNATIVES FOR
         THE FUTURE. New York: McGraw-Hill,
         1977.

         Gompert as editor for this book arranged
         for four other writers to think through
         the situation of what nuclear weapons will
         pose for international peace and progress
         through the 1980s. Each approached the
         same set of circumstances and presented
         very different responses and conclusions
         in a thought provoking manner. The author,
         in a concluding essay, wraps everything up
         and places the other four essays into
         perspective. Due to the caliber of the
         writing and the serious consideration
         required to understand the greater question,
         this is a book for the advanced nuclear
         reader.

107.   Halacy, Dan. NUCLEAR ENERGY. New York:
          Franklin Watts, 1978.

          Directed toward the junior high reader,
          this is an outstanding starter book on
          nuclear energy. Anyone unfamiliar with
          nuclear power will have a basic understand-
          ing of things nuclear after reading this
          book. Contents include brief discussions
          of atomic power, nuclear fuel, how a
          nuclear power plant operates, the dangers
          of nuclear energy, and a chronology of
          nuclear energy development. A useful
          reading guide for further study follows
          the text.

108.   Hellmann, Richard, and Caroline J.C.
          Hellmann. THE COMPETITIVE ECONOMICS
          OF NUCLEAR AND COAL POWER. Lexington,
          MA: Lexington Books, 1983.

          The authors, both economists, analyze
          the economics of nuclear and coal power
          plants which have been newly ordered and
          are expected to begin operation between
          1985 and 1995. The problem of underesti-
          mating construction costs and cost over-
          runs is a dilemma shared by the architect,
          the engineers, the manufacturers, and the
          public. Although this is a financial study
          of the industry, and therefore economically
          technical, general readers will find it
          useful for a look at how management views
          the cost problem and for comparing the
          nuclear vs. coal power question. Many
          charts, graphs, and tables accompany the
          text. The book covers the design and
          technological risks of nuclear power, the
          human factors, waste disposal, the decom-

missioning process, and several case
studies like the AEC, ERDA, NRC, and Exxon
cost studies.

109.   International Scientific Forum on an
        Acceptable Nuclear Energy Future of the
        World. NUCLEAR ENERGY AND ALTERNATIVES.
        Cambridge, MA: Ballinger, 1978.

        This work comprises the proceedings of a
conference held from November 7-11, 1977
at the Center for Theoretical Studies of
the University of Miami. Nearly fifty
educators, scientists, industrialists, and
governmental leaders participated by
presenting papers at this international
forum on nuclear energy. Some of the
papers may be considered highly technical
but there are plenty which the well-
informed reader can comprehend. In this
latter category is a series of papers
devoted to a worldwide energy inventory,
health and safety matters, the nuclear
proliferation controversy, and solar energy
as an alternative. The conference may not
go down in history as a landmark symposium
but, nevertheless, many of the papers
presented are noteworthy and somewhat controversial. This balanced collection does
contribute to a better understanding of
the greater nuclear power question.

110.   IS NUCLEAR POWER SAFE? Washington, DC:
          American Enterprise Institute, 1975.

          This small book is the edited transcript
          of an American Enterprise Institute Round
          Table discussion which was moderated by
          Melvin Laird, former Secretary of the
          Defense. The five participants were Ralph
          Nader, consumer advocate; Ralph Lapp,
          physicist; Craig Hosmer, former California
          Congressman; and Lawrence Moss, nuclear
          engineer and former Sierra Club president.
          This mix of people in the same room pre-
          sents a potential volatile situation but
          they do manage a most civil discourse on
          the nuclear safety issue. Although this
          is brief, useful and potent arguments are
          given for and against the continued use of
          nuclear power.

111.   Kaku, Michio, and Jennifer Trainer, eds.
          NUCLEAR POWER: BOTH SIDES: THE BEST
          ARGUMENTS FOR AND AGAINST THE MOST
          CONTROVERSIAL TECHNOLOGY. New York:
          Norton, 1982.

          This anthology provides a well-balanced
          analysis of the nuclear power debate
          through it twenty-five contributed essays.
          Most of the writers are vocal proponents
          or critics of the nuclear industry and
          each is probably represented elsewhere in
          this bibliography with his or her own book.
          This would be another excellent first book
          to read on the nuclear power controversy.

112.   Kuhn, James W. SCIENTIFIC AND MANAGERIAL
        POWER IN THE NUCLEAR INDUSTRY. New
        York: Columbia University Press, 1966.
        Foreword by Eli Ginzberg.

Here is a work which examines the extent
to which manpower influenced the development of the new technology pre-World War II.
Most of these gifted scientists (refugees
from Hitler and Mussolini) were responsible
for the harnessing of nuclear energy in
America. In fact, the atomic bomb itself
and the successful conclusion to World
War II can be attributed to this talented
group of foreign-born scientists. In later
years the development of peaceful nuclear
power became an interdisciplinary project
involving a diverse group of scientists
and mathematicians. Professor Kuhn also
discusses the role and errors that American
corporations made when hiring engineers to
direct the company research in nuclear
power. He surmises that management lacked
the necessary technical competence to
understand their role and the associated
risks, so they merely handed over the
decision making powers to the technical
staffs. In so doing they lost touch and
often did not understand what they were
getting into until it was too late, and
perhaps too costly to back out. Also
covered is the critical role that Admiral
Hyman Rickover played in the development
of nuclear power, the problems facing the
utility companies, and the skill obso-
lescence that occurs early in research and
development groups. This work is a
significant historical document of the
decision making powers behind the present
nuclear industry.

113.   Lewis, Richard S. THE NUCLEAR POWER
            REBELLION: CITIZENS VS. THE ATOMIC
            INDUSTRIAL ESTABLISHMENT. New York:
            Viking, 1972.

        In a narrative format Richard Lewis
    covers numerous events in the young history
    of atomic energy. Most of the incidents
    detail the involvement of the "down on the
    farm" citizenry and their reactions to a
    nuclear power plant in their backyard.
    Many court cases are highlighted for easy
    interpretation. Interesting commentary is
    provided on radiation hazards and on the
    move to build breeder reactors.

114.   Martin, Laurence, ed. STRATEGIC THOUGHT
            IN THE NUCLEAR AGE. Baltimore: Johns
            Hopkins University, 1980.

        Some interesting and challenging argu-
    ments are presented in the seven contri-
    buted essays which comprise *Strategic
    Thought*. As a whole the essays record
    strategic thought since 1945 on a global
    scale and in light of a growing nuclear
    arsenal. Topics covered include the util-
    ity of the military in world politics, the
    economics of national security, threat as
    perceived in the intelligence process,
    limited war from minimal to nuclear, the
    history of strategic forces and targeting,
    managing international crises, and arms
    control. All authors concur that military
    strength is a fact of life and that arms
    will not go away. A concern is expressed
    that governments learn to manage via arms
    control, not the elimination of arms which
    could probably never be achieved in most of
    our lifetimes. Numerous methods for
    increased arms control and the many bar-
    riers which exist are analyzed. The ideas
    presented in this book are not necessarily

new and innovative but they are presented
in a readable, professional manner.

115. Metzger, H. Peter. THE ATOMIC ESTABLISH-
MENT. New York: Simon & Schuster,
1972.

This is a historically valuable work in
that the author shows how the U.S. Congress
and the Atomic Energy Commission changed
from enemies to friends. Indepth discussions are provided on nuclear weapons and
radioactive waste with several solutions
for their management being offered.
Metzger suggests that the problems we have
today with nuclear energy are not technical
ones, but rather they are politically
rooted. This is a hefty volume of easy
reading for those with a nuclear interest.

116. Moss, Thomas H., and David L. Sills.
THE THREE MILE ISLAND NUCLEAR ACCIDENT:
LESSONS AND IMPLICATIONS. New York:
New York Academy of Sciences, 1981.
(Annals of the New York Academy of
Sciences, v. 365)

In 1980 the New York Academy of Sciences
held a conference on the nuclear incident
at Three Mile Island. The keynote theme
was that "the central problem of nuclear
energy is not waste disposal or even the
connection between proliferation and
nuclear power. It is, rather, reactor
safety", according to Alvin Weinberg. The
conference was attended by many of the same
people who were touched by the accident
just one year earlier and who were now

present to give their personal views.
Discussions centered on the technical
history of the accident, the predicted
likelihood of such an event, the radiation
released, the problem of decontaminating
the site, the behavior of individuals and
organizations involved, and the attitudes
of the local residents. A most interesting
segment deals with the relationship between
the nuclear authorities and the press. To
the anti-nuclear people TMI showed that the
industry operates on the brink of disaster.
To the nuclear proponents it merely con-
firmed the safety of the system. One
question which was asked at the conference
was whether we should reconsider the gas-
cooled reactor, one which depends less on
engineered safety features and more on
inherent characteristics to prevent accidents.

117.   Nero, Anthony V.   A GUIDEBOOK TO NUCLEAR
        REACTORS. Berkeley: University of
        California Press, 1979.

        Informative, rather than argumentative,
this book explains the major features of
reactors and the issues surrounding their
use. The book begins with an outline of
the main features of a nuclear power plant
and explains the effect which reactors
have on their environment. Many pages are
devoted to discussions of pressurized water
reactors, boiling water reactors, heavy
water reactors, and gas-cooled thermal
reactors. Nero also considers the sources
of uranium and the various nuclear fuel
cycles. Under the premise that nuclear
power demands will accelerate at a slow
pace in the U.S., the author provides
figures which should help to decide how
much nuclear power is needed, in what form,

and which type of reactor is best suited to
that need. The focus is on reactor systems
found in, or of interest to the United
States. This means that the many British,
French, and Russian reactor types are miss-
ing from this guidebook. Dr. Nero has provided the non-scientist with a concise
source of information on a variety of
nuclear systems all the while relating them
to the controversial issues of safety,
waste, and weapons.

118.   NUCLEAR POWER IN AMERICAN THOUGHT.
        Washington, DC: Edison Electric Insti-
        tute, 1980. (Decisionmakers Bookshelf
        Series, v. 8)

        In an approach very different from
other books in this bibliography, *Nuclear
Power in American Thought* handles the
nuclear power debate with non-technical
arguments involving ethics, history, philosophy, politics, and psychology. The book
is a collection of four essays which attempt
to show how these humanistic concerns affect
and will continue to affect American thought
on the nuclear issue. Contributors are
Dr. Andrew Hacker, a professor of political
science; Dr. Robert L. DuPont, psychiatrist
and president of the non-profit Institute
for Behavior and Health, Inc.; Dr. William
Barrett, a professor of philosophy; and Dr.
Margaret Maxey, Assistant Director of the
South Carolina Energy Research Institute.
With such an intellectual group of authors
one might expect a work that is untouchable
by most general readers but such is not the
case. The essay by Dr. DuPont on nuclear
phobia is outstanding as are William Barrett's
predictions on the American acceptance of
nuclear power.

119.   Oak Ridge Associated Universities. Institute
        for Energy Analysis. ECONOMIC AND
        ENVIRONMENTAL IMPACTS OF A U.S. MORA-
        TORIUM, 1985-2010. Cambridge, MA:
        MIT, 1979.

        Numerous futurists contributed to the
        research and conclusions in this book which
        examines the impact of a nuclear freeze.
        Five distinct economic implications are
        observed: future cost of electricity,
        regional dislocations, the nuclear industry
        impacts, the effect on the coal industry,
        and the international impacts. Some of the
        conclusions derived include the prediction
        that energy demand will increase at a slow
        rate and that nuclear power is cheaper than
        fossil-generated power in most areas of the
        U.S. It is also understood that a nuclear
        moratorium will require that more coal be
        mined and the burning of this coal will
        increase emissions into the air, perhaps
        changing the worldwide climate. Dozens of
        tables, charts, and figures are provided to
        help you draw your own conclusions. How-
        ever, all of these studies and predictions
        cannot answer the question, what will be
        the energy supply and demand beyond the year
        2010?

120.   Patterson, Walter C. NUCLEAR POWER.
        Baltimore, MD: Penguin, 1976.

        This small paperback may be used as a
        starting point on the path to developing a
        nuclear awareness. In very simple terms
        the elements of the nuclear predicament are
        explained as they relate to history, costs,
        reactors, and the future. An attempt is
        made to answer many of the pressing

questions and an ample reading list is
provided for further clarification.

121.   Peat, David F.   THE NUCLEAR BOOK.   Ottawa,
            Canada: Deneau and Greenberg, 1979.

            Canadian scientist and journalist
David Peat has written this book as a guide
to nuclear safety in Canada. The Three Mile
Island incident prompted Canadians to look
more closely at their CANDU (Canadian-Deu-
terium-Uranium) reactor, a heavy-water
reactor considered to be safe and reliable.
The CANDU reactor is compared to other types
of reactors worldwide in terms of safety,
economics, energy demands, and the technology which is available. Peat explains why,
in his opinion, the CANDU reactor was the
best choice for Canada at the time. This
work also provides elementary descriptions
of nuclear reactors, waste, risk, nuclear
industry regulations, alternatives for the
future, and many more critical issues.

122.   Pringle, Laurence.   NUCLEAR POWER: FROM
            PHYSICS TO POLITICS.   New York:
            Macmillan, 1979.

            The development of nuclear power is
traced from Hiroshima and Nagasaki to the
present day with predictions for the year
2000. Readers are informed of the secrecy
surrounding the development of atomic power
and explore decades of governmental confusion as to who promotes and who regulates
nuclear power. With this as a background,
Pringle looks at the controversy itself and
presents both sides of the question to
readers. This is a very easy-to-read high
school level book with many photographs.

123.   Shrader-Frechette, K.S. NUCLEAR POWER
        AND PUBLIC POLICY: THE SOCIAL AND
        ETHICAL PROBLEMS OF FISSION TECHNOLOGY.
        Dordrecht, Holland: D. Reidel, 1980.

        A variety of problems are presented as
        the author examines the social, political,
        and ethical issues which have heretofore
        been ignored by the government when making
        nuclear power assessments. The author
        argues that the current policy regarding
        nuclear technology is unjust, that to
        generate long-lived nuclear wastes is
        reprehensible, and that a core meltdown
        is improbable on both logical and
        scientific grounds. Very brief coverage
        is given to the economics of nuclear power
        and nuclear safety.

124.   Stephens, Mark. THREE MILE ISLAND. New
        York: Random House, 1981.

        This is essentially a detailed chronicle
        of what happened during the last week of
        March 1979 at Three Mile Island. In a
        very matter of fact style the author
        relates the occurrences going on inside
        the power plant and how the Nuclear Regu-
        latory Commission and other public
        officials responded. Some commentary on
        how the press covered the affair and their
        antagonistic relationship with the offi-
        cials is included. The author's conclusion
        is that TMI officials and the state and
        national regulatory agencies considered
        the chance of an accident so remote that
        they were really unprepared to deal with
        the incident or to even protect the
        people.

125.   TOSCA: THE TOTAL SOCIAL COST OF COAL AND
          NUCLEAR POWER. Linda Gaines, R. Stephen
          Berry, and Thomas V. Long, eds.
          Cambridge, MA: Ballinger, 1979.

          Social costs are defined as the direct
          cost of generating power combined with the
          indirect costs of human health, the
          environment, waste, etc. TOSCA includes a
          model for estimating these social costs of
          coal and nuclear power generation to the
          year 2004. The authors discuss research
          and development expenditures and venture a
          controversial claim that pressurized water
          and boiling reactors are identical. This
          work is primarily concerned with the econo-
          mic factors of power generation and the
          discussion of the model which the authors
          have developed. The value of the book lies
          in its use as an energy reference and for
          those hard-to-find cost comparisons.

126.   Webb, Richard E. THE ACCIDENT HAZARDS OF
          NUCLEAR POWER PLANTS. Amherst, MA:
          University of Massachusetts Press, 1976.

          Four classes of reactor accidents in
          which the fuel could overheat and other
          accidents which may be caused by design and
          error are graphically presented. The topic
          of nuclear sabotage is briefly discussed as
          is the controversial Rasmussen Report, a
          congressional reactor safety study. The
          author stresses the value of nuclear power
          as an alternative fuel but cautions that we
          should assess the hazards first to deter-
          mine whether or not the risks are accept-
          able. The negative aspects of nuclear power
          may appear to be the stronger element but
          Webb does present an equally balanced,
          unbiased report of nuclear power.

127.   Weiss, Ann E. THE NUCLEAR QUESTION.
          New York: Harcourt Brace Jovanovich,
          1981.

          Aimed at the high school aged or the
          uninformed reader, *The Nuclear Question*
          summarizes the story of nuclear power from
          its promise, development, costs, benefits,
          and dangers. Briefly covered are some of
          the events which led to the present day
          debate over the use of nuclear power. An
          even balance of arguments for and against
          nuclear power are provided. Numerous
          questions about the future of nuclear power
          and other sources of energy complete this
          introduction to the nuclear controversy.

128.   United States. President's Commission on
          the Accident at Three Mile Island.
          THE NEED FOR CHANGE, THE LEGACY OF TMI:
          REPORT OF THE PRESIDENT'S COMMISSION ON
          THE ACCIDENT AT THREE MILE ISLAND.
          Washington, DC: U.S. Government Printing
          Office, 1979.

          Two weeks after the TMI incident Presi-
          dent Carter appointed a twelve member com-
          mission to complete a comprehensive study
          of the event. Dr. John G. Kemeny, Presi-
          dent of Dartmouth College, chaired the
          Commission which was charged with making a
          technical assessment of the events and
          their causes, to analyze the management, to
          evaluate the response of the Nuclear Regu-
          latory Commission and other emergency pre-
          paredness authorities, to assess the flow
          of information concerning the events at TMI,
          and to make appropriate recommendations.
          The findings and the recommendations of the
          Commission are too numerous to list here
          but the general tone is one of suspicion
          and concern over the practices of the NRC.
          Numerous photos, an account of the accident,

and a staff list is appended to the
report.

129. Winter, John, and David Conner. POWER
      PLANT SITING. New York: Van Nostrand
      Reinhold, 1978.

      Although primarily geared to the archi-
      tects and engineers who are concerned with
      the siting process, this book is valuable
      to others as a guide to understanding the
      care, analysis, and study which goes along
      with site selection. The viewpoints of the
      public, the utility companies, and the
      governmental regulatory agencies are con-
      sidered. The book is thorough in its
      discussions of the energy crisis, legisla-
      tion, land and sea siting possibilities,
      nuclear concerns, power plant design, and
      future considerations. Many charts as well
      as a sample environmental impact statement
      accompany the text.

Author Index

Subject Index

Title Index